D1032927

VOLUME
17

Originally published in the United Kingdom in weekly parts **COMBAT & SURVIVAL** is a study of the armed forces at work. It shows the skills taught to soldiers and the way in which military units operate. It examines the weapons and equipment used by different armies; and, by looking at recruit training and exercises, **COMBAT & SURVIVAL** demonstrates how the armed forces develop individual responsibility, leadership and initiative.

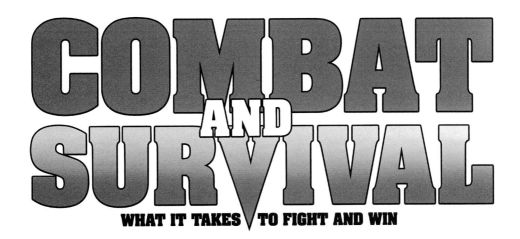

COMBAT AND SURVIVAL

WHAT IT TAKES TO FIGHT AND WIN

VOLUME
17

H. S. STUTTMAN, INC. *publishers*   Westport, Connecticut 06889

Contents
Volume 17

Published by H. S. STUTTMAN INC.
Westport, Connecticut 06889
© Aerospace Publishing 1991
ISBN 0-87475-560-3

All individual combat and personal survival activities involve
risk or injury, to oneself and others, and great care must be taken in
carrying out any such activities. Expert guidance should be sought
and equipment checked for reliability before any activities described
in this work are carried out. The publishers cannot assume responsibility
for damage to property or injury, death or loss to persons which may
result from carrying out the activities described in this work. In carrying out
any activities described in this work, persons do so entirely at their own risk.
PRINTED IN THE UNITED STATES OF AMERICA

1P(1632)30

FIGHTING IN THE STREETS

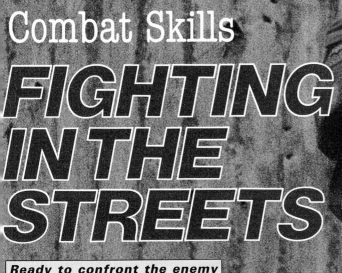

Ready to confront the enemy hand to hand at any moment, under constant threat from sniper fire, hacking your way through a heavily-defended city takes skill, stamina and patience. You have to fight from room to room, house to house, and street to street to secure your objective. It's an infantryman's job, for in these conditions armour and artillery can offer you little support. This introduction to the British Army's approach to fighting in built-up areas (FIBUA) surveys the special nature, principles and weaponry of this kind of combat.

Principles into practice

The general principles of attack and defence hold good for operations in built-up areas. How you put these principles into practice will depend on whether you are fighting in a small village, a collection of farm buildings or in a large city.

You'll be fighting mainly on your own. Tanks and field guns may be devastatingly effective at close quarters but are often impossible to manoeuvre or bring to bear in city streets. In the end, the infantryman has to finish the job, by fighting at a very low level – at platoon or section strength. To try to carry out some great plan at company or battalion level in the streets of a large city would be very difficult.

A platoon sergeant equipped with a dummy 'mouse holing' charge prepares to move forward with the reserve section during an exercise in Imber village. The real charge is a wooden cross with PE4 explosive at the end of each leg. It will blow man-sized holes in exterior walls.

Inexperienced soldiers fondly imagine that anti-tank weapons such as the 66-mm will blow large holes in a house. But the HEAT warhead is designed to punch small holes in tank targets, and that is all it does: punch small holes.

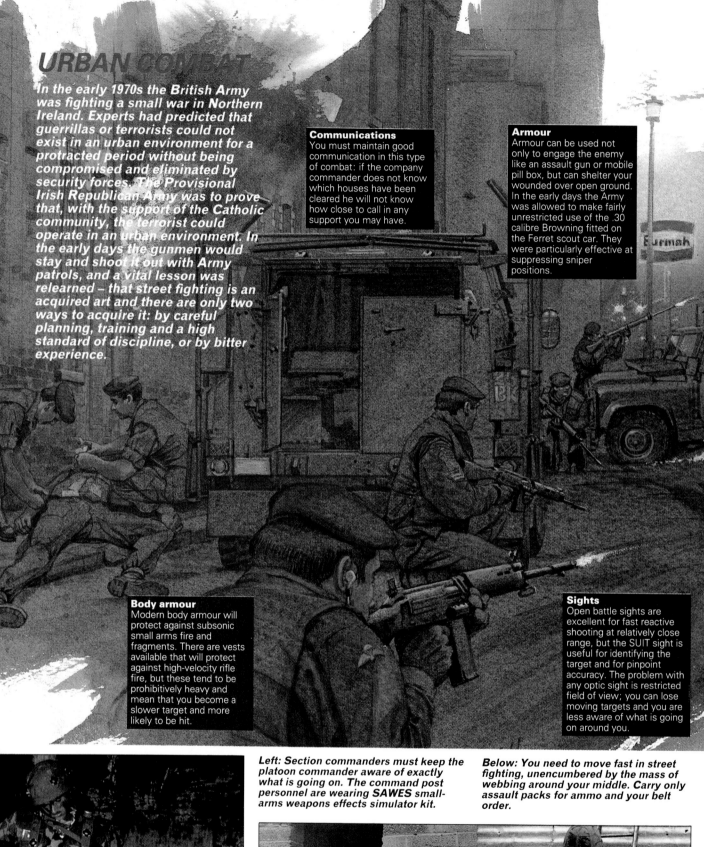

URBAN COMBAT

In the early 1970s the British Army was fighting a small war in Northern Ireland. Experts had predicted that guerrillas or terrorists could not exist in an urban environment for a protracted period without being compromised and eliminated by security forces. The Provisional Irish Republican Army was to prove that, with the support of the Catholic community, the terrorist could operate in an urban environment. In the early days the gunmen would stay and shoot it out with Army patrols, and a vital lesson was relearned – that street fighting is an acquired art and there are only two ways to acquire it: by careful planning, training and a high standard of discipline, or by bitter experience.

Communications
You must maintain good communication in this type of combat: if the company commander does not know which houses have been cleared he will not know how close to call in any support you may have.

Armour
Armour can be used not only to engage the enemy like an assault gun or mobile pill box, but can shelter your wounded over open ground. In the early days the Army was allowed to make fairly unrestricted use of the .30 calibre Browning fitted on the Ferret scout car. They were particularly effective at suppressing sniper positions.

Body armour
Modern body armour will protect against subsonic small arms fire and fragments. There are vests available that will protect against high-velocity rifle fire, but these tend to be prohibitively heavy and mean that you become a slower target and more likely to be hit.

Sights
Open battle sights are excellent for fast reactive shooting at relatively close range, but the SUIT sight is useful for identifying the target and for pinpoint accuracy. The problem with any optic sight is restricted field of view; you can lose moving targets and you are less aware of what is going on around you.

*Left: Section commanders must keep the platoon commander aware of exactly what is going on. The command post personnel are wearing **SAWES** small-arms weapons effects simulator kit.*

Below: You need to move fast in street fighting, unencumbered by the mass of webbing around your middle. Carry only assault packs for ammo and your belt order.

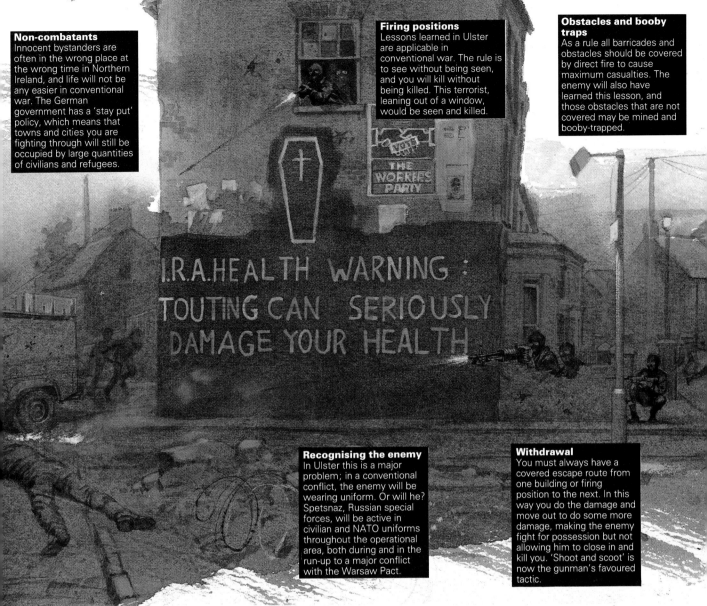

Non-combatants
Innocent bystanders are often in the wrong place at the wrong time in Northern Ireland, and life will not be any easier in conventional war. The German government has a 'stay put' policy, which means that towns and cities you are fighting through will still be occupied by large quantities of civilians and refugees.

Firing positions
Lessons learned in Ulster are applicable in conventional war. The rule is to see without being seen, and you will kill without being killed. This terrorist, leaning out of a window, would be seen and killed.

Obstacles and booby traps
As a rule all barricades and obstacles should be covered by direct fire to cause maximum casualties. The enemy will also have learned this lesson, and those obstacles that are not covered may be mined and booby-trapped.

I.R.A. HEALTH WARNING : TOUTING CAN SERIOUSLY DAMAGE YOUR HEALTH

THE WORKERS PARTY

Recognising the enemy
In Ulster this is a major problem; in a conventional conflict, the enemy will be wearing uniform. Or will he? Spetsnaz, Russian special forces, will be active in civilian and NATO uniforms throughout the operational area, both during and in the run-up to a major conflict with the Warsaw Pact.

Withdrawal
You must always have a covered escape route from one building or firing position to the next. In this way you do the damage and move out to do some more damage, making the enemy fight for possession but not allowing him to close in and kill you. 'Shoot and scoot' is now the gunman's favoured tactic.

A special kind of warfare

Conventional warfare and FIBUA are markedly different in a number of ways.

1 You will be fighting at very close quarters. The enemy will be a house or a street away, sometimes only a room away, or the other side of a wall. You will have to be prepared for hand to hand fighting. Your reactions will have to be instantaneous, for there will be no second chances.

2 It is always difficult to locate the source of enemy fire in a built-up area. The 'crack' and 'thump' of a high velocity round echoes and re-echoes off surrounding buildings, so that it's virtually impossible to tell where it has been fired from. You will also find it difficult to locate fire, as a well-drilled defender will site his weapons back from windows and doors.

You will be further confused by the smoke and dust which collects and hangs in the streets. Even when you do identify a target, it's difficult to point it out to your comrades. The only really reliable way is with tracer.

Close fighting

3 Your fields of fire and observation will be much more restricted than you are used to, and the enemy enjoys better cover and concealment than in most types of countryside. You, as the attacker, must expose yourself in order to make progress. This leaves you prey to snipers, who are particularly effective in an urban environment. They are usually so well hidden that you're unlikely to be able to get an aimed shot at them. The best answer is to fire an anti-tank weapon at the window or part of the house you think the fire is coming from. Overkill perhaps, but effective nevertheless.

4 Tanks can give very effective close support, but they must be protected by infantry. If a tank ventures along an enemy-held street before you have cleared the houses on either side, the enemy can fire an anti-tank weapon into the side or rear of the tank at very close quarters.

5 A particular characteristic of fighting in built-up areas is the appalling quality of VHF radio communications. Although you can place remote aerials on tops of buildings, reliable communications at section and platoon level are very difficult in a dense urban environment. You will have to use light signals, communication chords, flags or any other suitable method of communication.

6 There are likely to be civilians in the midst of an urban battle. Their presence will obviously complicate your execution of operations.

Do's and don'ts

There are also some special rules that you should remember when you conduct offensive operations in a built-up area. First, because of the complexity of the task, your plan must be simple and progressive. A step by step approach is usually best.

Combat Skills

Second, you must be prepared to delegate control to a greater extent than perhaps you might otherwise. In most tactical situations you can see most of your unit and control it accordingly. In a village or town you cannot. Actions tend to be small, independent actions, at section or even individual level.

Commanders must therefore keep well forward. Divide your tactical area into sectors, and give platoons and sections limited objectives within these sectors.

Third, you must be extremely thorough when clearing buildings. Every room, cellar and attic must be checked and rechecked. It is a dangerous and slow business, but absolutely vital.

Tanks and sappers

Fourth, use supporting arms and weapons to the maximum. You should use artillery and mortars to soften up the enemy before an assault. Tanks are particularly effective in supporting infantry in built-up areas,

blowing entry holes in buildings with their main armament, supporting an infantry assault with their machine guns and giving cover to men crossing open bullet-swept spaces.

Vulnerable in towns

Tanks are particularly vulnerable, however, in built-up areas. Protecting infantry must clear houses that could be a threat to their supporting tanks.

Engineer support is most important in a damaged built-up area. Rubble will have to be cleared by bulldozers, routes will have to be cleared for vehicles, mines will have to be detected and removed and booby traps disarmed in captured buildings. Sappers are experts at bridging obstacles, removing obstacles and creating obstacles. All these areas of expertise will be useful in built-up areas.

The kit for the job

Special equipment and weapons are invaluable in FIBUA. The British Army is not at present equipped with flamethrowers. The Soviet and US

Stores for street fighting

Weapons

In addition to the normal range of infantry weapons, the following have been found useful:

1 120-mm Wombat anti-tank weapon
2 Flame weapons
3 84-mm MAW
4 Mouse-holing charges
5 Satchel demolition charges
6 Shotguns
7 Sub-machine guns
8 Pistols (for very enclosed places)
9 Sniper rifles, with the snipers to use them
10 Grenade-launchers
11 51-mm mortar
12 66-mm LAW

Note: The 7.62-mm NATO bullet is far more effective than 5.56-mm rounds in an urban environment. The GPMG is quite capable of shooting a hole big enough for an entry point in house brick walls.

Ammunition

You need as many grenades as you can comfortably move with, plus extensive resupply of grenades and small-arms ammo. Here 5.56mm ammunition has the advantage of being considerably lighter than 7.62mm, and is easier to use in a close-quarter battle environment. You also need:

1 White phosphorus and ordinary smoke grenades
2 CS gas canisters
3 Tracer ammunition for target indications

Equipment

1 Assault ladders
2 Rope
3 Caving ladders
4 Torches
5 Grappling hooks
6 Extra field dressings

Left: The British Army is horribly outgunned in flame warfare. The Soviets have developed a wide range of flame weapons from hand-held to tank-mounted (in the case of this T54/55).

Below: The British Army does not have a purpose-built assault weapon, but the US have always seen the value in these weapons for urban combat. This is a prototype shoulder-launched multi-purpose assault weapon, in service with the Marine Corps as a bunker buster.

armies are, and they are intended in particular for FIBUA. The Soviets, Germans, British and Americans all used flamethrowers during World War II and found them to be the most effective method of clearing bunkers and buildings.

The other useful weapon system is the grenade launcher, which projects high explosive grenades through windows, doors and other cavities in enemy-held buildings.

Perhaps your most urgent need is to blow entry holes in the sides of buildings. In the absence of tank support this is vital. At present, the British Army has to use the Carl Gustav medium anti-tank weapon or Milan anti-tank guided missile to do the job. Both are designed to penetrate armour, a different requirement, but they nevertheless will have some effect.

Finally, climbing aids such as ladders and grapnels are invaluable. Often you'll find it's impossible to enter a building via the ground floor, and so you will need a quick method of getting into a second floor window.

The art of fighting in built-up areas is a developing and topical one. Europe is becoming rapidly urbanised, and any future conflict is likely to be fought mainly in built-up areas.

Above: An Loc, South Vietnam, clearly demonstrates the scale of destruction involved in urban combat, after two months of desperate fighting and 50,000 rounds of NVA artillery.

Below: Members of the Parachute Regiment Home Service Force demonstrate their POW handling skills. Don't weaken your assault sections to provide POW handlers.

TO BOMB OR NOT TO BOMB

Bombing can be extremely counter-productive unless the assault troops can go in as soon as the town has been hit.

Su-25 'Frogfoots' drop parachute retarded bombs on an Afghan village just prior to an assault by ground forces. The bombing provides adequate warning to clear out.

Combat Report
Vietnam:
Incidents at Tan Son Nhut

Thomas Young served in the US Air Force Police in Vietnam. Here he describes two incidents on the perimeter of Tan Son Nhut air base.

It was January 1971, and I had been assigned to working on the flight line. This involved sitting in a box surrounded by sandbags with two or three other guards. Two guards were placed on the M-60 machine-gun; one had to check the ID cards, and one had to watch him and man the radio. This was virtually impossible during a full-scale rocket attack. Soldiers would come through on foot, in jeeps and even on bikes, and you had to try to glance at their ID cards as they went past. But once you'd been on the flight line for some time you got to know most of the men.

One day this Major drives up

Some of the officers, though, liked to play games in order to check our security. This was to be expected, but not in the middle of a full-scale rocket attack. There was one officer in particular who had several different access badges. Most of the guys knew him, except me. So there we were one day checking IDs, with rockets whizzing overhead and the rain pouring down, when this Major drives up and flashes his badge at me so quickly that I barely had time to see the colour, much less who it belonged to.

I pointed my rifle and asked the driver to pull up and step out for a proper ID check. Devenski had also noticed that something was wrong and swung his M-60 towards the jeep. I was using the radio when the officer started using his rank on me. Being new and only an AIC, I hesitated for a couple of seconds before remembering what I'd been taught: NO MATTER WHAT RANK HE OR SHE IS, YOU ARE IN CHARGE. So I said, "Please be quiet, sir, while I check with the desk."

He didn't, he just got worse, so I said, "Spread-eagled on the ground, sir."

Remember, it was raining hard. His driver was winking at me all the time, trying to tell me what

Despite stringent security the air bases continued to receive mortar and rocket attacks.

was going on. I didn't take any notice. I simply put my M-16 on auto and pointed it at both of them. Immediately the driver was flat on his face in the mud, while the officer knelt and yelled that this was just a test. I repeated the command, and he continued to complain. I had to smile. Devenski's mouth was wide open; he couldn't believe it.

He covered them while I walked back into the shack to radio for an SAT team to take them away. I knew I could catch hell for this, but it was what I had been trained for, and we were in the middle of a war zone and a rocket attack. After that the officer must have found out when I was on duty, because I only saw him one other time. I passed him coming out of the mess hall, and saluted him and said, "Good morning, sir," with a little smile on my face. He was a full bird Colonel with the law enforcement section.

As well as the law enforcement cops and security cops there were the dog handlers. These guys mainly worked at night, on perimeter duty, and were on call the whole time. A friend of mine from South Carolina was a dog handler on the perimeter. Kevin loved his dog, which was a German Shepherd called Adolf.

He had run into VC

The SAT teams would often drive dog and handler out at night if one of their own trucks were unavailable. One night, after dropping off Kevin and Adolf, we were making our rounds on the flight line when we got a call saying that Kevin had run into trouble.

We got near the area, left the truck with one man to monitor the radio, and fanned out to find Kevin. He had gone too far out and had run into VC. He was pinned down when two of us reached him. The first thing he said was that Adolf had gone. I thought he must be dead, but Kevin said no. He had broken free from his harness when the firing started and had run for the tree line. Kevin had tried to follow him, but had to back out because of the shooting.

At this moment two more teams arrived, so we called in chopper cover and proceeded forwards, hoping the chopper would flush the VC towards us. We had made the treeline and spread out, watching for VC and booby traps. A

Dogs serving in Vietnam included Air Force sentinels guarding the airbases as well as scout dogs and combat trackers that went on patrol.

couple of VC broke cover and ran, one towards Sergeant Dunn's position. Kevin and I turned and fired, getting both of them and almost getting Dunn. The choppers were strafing the area in front of us.

We heard growling

All the time Kevin was calling for Adolf, but there was still no sign. We advanced a couple of hundred feet further, but figured that the VC had broken contact and left, so we ended the alert.

We were heading back to our lines when we heard growling. We all hit the dirt, except for Kevin, who knew his dog's voice. We told him to hold off and just call him, but it was too late: Kevin had already disappeared into the dense bush. We only followed when Kevin gave the all clear, but we stayed apart and alert.

There was Adolf, teeth bared, standing on a VC officer, and breathing hard. He didn't want to move, and Kevin had to put the harness on him to pull him off. Our unit didn't get many prisoners, so this was a treat for us. Aside from a few teethmarks the VC was all right – just scared **** – and Adolf received a special award for bravery.

HOUSE CLEARING DRILLS

In street fighting, occupying enemy forces seem to have everything on their side — cover, confusion, booby traps, heavily fortified buildings — and you have no choice but to expose yourself to these hazards if you're to complete the job properly and clear them out. But careful planning and preparation, skill and patience will massively reduce the risks — and help ensure your mission's success. This section of the Combat Skills series tells you how to equip and ready yourself for fighting in built-up areas, and how to clear a house in section or platoon strength.

Plan fighting in built-up areas (FIBUA) in detail from whatever maps, air photographs, town plans or other intelligence you have available. Having studied the information, the commander should divide the area into sectors and allocate each one to a company or combat team.

Basic equipment

Before you become involved in the messy business of street fighting, you will need to prepare your equipment, ammunition and medical plans minutely. You should drop off any bulky equipment such as packs, bergens or entrenching tools so that you can fit through narrow holes, passages and doors, and move a great deal faster in any circumstances.

Carry as many torches as possible to search the inside of buildings; binoculars are also useful to look into windows and other dark areas, since they increase the light available. Toggle ropes, grapnels and ladders are absolutely vital. Better than rope ladders are aluminium assault ladders. They can be placed against an upstairs window and you can be inside the building in seconds.

Arms and ammunition

Think about what ammunition you should take with you into a house-clearing or street-clearing operation. You will use a lot of ammunition in FIBUA operations, and you should ensure that every man has more than enough before committing him to battle. Every man should carry extra grenades, and some a grenade launcher. This is most important.

A 12-year-old ARVN airborne trooper poses with his M79 40-mm grenade launcher. The M79 is an excellent weapon for street fighting: with a little practice you can put an HE grenade through a window at 200 metres.

The GPMG is the weapon for covering an assault on a house. If the building is unprepared you could kill the enemy with shoot-throughs.

FIGHTING IN BUILT-UP AREAS

Successful house-clearing depends on thorough prior planning, efficient drills for moving from room to room, full use of fire and movement, a very high standard of leadership, and the one factor without which everything else is redundant: fighting spirit.

You will also need tracer rounds. In the confusion of a built-up area, you'll find it particularly difficult, sometimes impossible, to indicate targets accurately. By far the simplest way of doing this is to tell your section or battle partner to watch your tracer; when you fire, it will indicate precisely where the enemy is. If tracer is not available or if you have run out, a more detailed fire order may be necessary.

Make sure that you have a means of blowing holes in the sides of buildings

Inside the house
Once inside, it will be dark and you will be fighting the enemy on his ground. He may have changed the internal layout of the house to add to your confusion or channel you into a booby trap or onto his small-arms fire. The only thing you have on your side are the drills.

Speed
Once inside, progress from room to room as fast as possible until the house is completely clear of enemy and then reorganise quickly to defend it. If you delay, the enemy will counterattack and the expensive game of hide-and-seek will start all over again.

Entryman
It helps to use the small but nasty members of the section for this job. They must be aggressive: the fighting may be hand-to-hand and those that pause to think too long will lose the initiative and be killed. The larger members of the section will not move as fast through the enclosed spaces.

Link man
He must be very carefully briefed if you are to avoid being shot by your own men in the confusion of battle. His job is to pass orders from the commander in the house to the gun team commander outside. A can of spray paint is handy for marking entry points and rooms that have been cleared.

Reorganisation
When the covering group hear 'house clear' from the link man they must move up and in immediately, as this is the most vulnerable point in the attack. They must use the entry points already cleared by the assault group: going your own way in may lead to a mine or booby trap. Once all the section are inside, the section commander will allot soldiers to rooms and give out firing arcs.

The covering group
Their task is to blast the target to keep the enemy's head down so that the assault team can approach the house and then suppress the rooms that remain to be taken as the assault team work through the objective. Finally, they must cover any escape routes the defenders may have.

Limit the objective
A section can only take a very limited objective with any certainty: a single house or a few rooms. The platoon would only be expected to take out two or three houses.

INFANTRY WEAPONS EFFECTS

Projectile or weapon	Range in metres	Effect on different materials		
		Pine	Sand	Concrete
		Penetration in inches		
5.56mm ball	25	10.5	1.4	1.4
	100	22.4	3.7	1.3
	200	25.0	3.7	1.2
7.62mm NATO ball	25	13.1	5.2	2.3
	100	18.5	4.4	2.3
	200	41.7	7.4	2.3
50 calibre machine gun Ball	200	13.0 (oak)	14.0	1.0
50 calibre machine gun Armour piercing	200	n/a	14.0	2.0
LAW 66mm HEAT	All ranges	n/a	72.0	24.0
90mm recoiless rifle HEAT	All ranges	n/a	42.0	24.0
Dragon HEAT	All ranges	n/a	96.0	48.0

n/a: information not available

This photograph illustrates Lesson One of street fighting. If the enemy have left an entry point to a position open, it is not a mistake: it will be booby-trapped.

in order to gain entry. This could be an anti-tank weapon, or prepared frame charges. If you have tanks with you, they can do the job.

Prepare for casualties

Finally, you must make medical preparations, since casualties are likely to be high. Extra shell dressings and morphine should be carried by everyone. Take extra drinking water as far forward as possible, and keep stretcher bearers in reserve. You will have to make plans for evacuating casualties, and prisoners and local in-habitants as well. Civilians should be encouraged to remain off the streets and take refuge in cellars away from the immediate battle areas.

Having made all these preparations and plans, you can get on with the business of house-clearing. In this kind of fighting, you will be given limited objectives. A section is about the right size to tackle an average sized house. Platoons and sections can help each other by working in parallel, for instance down each side of a street.

You should organise your section as follows:
1 Section Commander
2 Assault Group: two entry men, two bombers and one lookout
3 Covering Group: Section Second in Command and machine-gunner

The drill for a section given this task is:
1 The covering group will take up a fire position to cover the point of entry and, if possible, cut off any enemy trying to escape.
2 As soon as the covering fire goes down, the bombers lob in a grenade and the two entrymen enter the house. If possible, enter the building from the top storey – never from the ground floor. You may have to blow a hole in the wall to gain entry. Once the entry-men are inside the house, they clear the room they have entered. They then indicate to the section commander, bombers and lookout that it is safe to follow.
3 The section commander, bombers and lookout enter the house. The

Snipers
There is nothing more effective than a sniper on ground that suits him. The rubble of a bombed and shelled town will be a sniper's paradise, and crossing open ground knowing that there is a hidden trained marksman who is shooting at you is paralysing.

SA80
The new rifle provides very considerable advantages over the SLR for street fighting, the most important of which is that the reduced weight of 5.56-mm means that it will be easier to carry the vast quantities of ammunition required. The optic sight is far better for pinpoint accuracy and the overall dimensions of the weapon means it can be brought to bear at speed in confined spaces.

HOW TO CLEAR A HOUSE

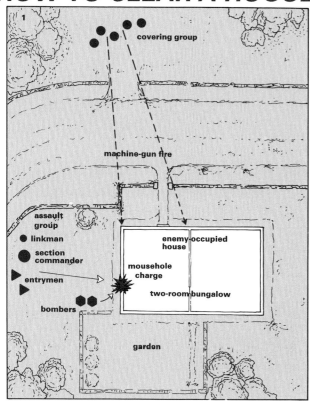

Under covering fire from the fire support group, the bombers from the assault group move forward and plant the mouse-holing charge on the exterior wall and take cover. As soon as the charge has gone off the assault group move up.

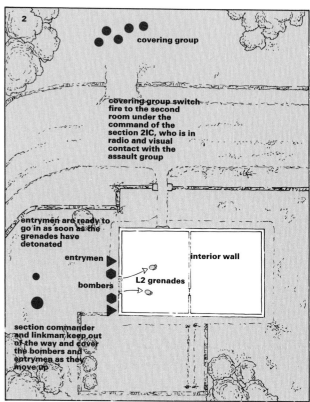

The bombers stand each side of the entry point with the entrymen next to them, and the bombers throw grenades in together. The section commander and link man keep out of it until the grenades have gone off. The move could be made under cover of smoke if it is exposed.

bombers then clear the house, room by room, storey by storey, from the roof to the cellar. The lookout remains by the original point of entry and keeps contact with the covering group.

4 When the house is clear, reorganise your section – inside or outside the house, depending on the next task.

Room by room

The drill for clearing parts of a building is:

1 Throw a grenade into a room and, immediately it has exploded, enter the room engaging the enemy with bullet and bayonet.

2 Fire into cupboards and other likely hiding places.

3 Shoot into the ceiling and the floor, to discourage any enemy who may be above or below.

4 When moving upstairs, do it quickly and with fire support, ideally from a tank machine gun or GPMG sited outside.

Platoon assault

If a platoon is given the task of clearing a building it will be organised as

THE ENTRY DRILL

Pick a blind approach to the house that gives maximum cover from fire and view and is at 90 degrees to your fire support. Decide where you are going to enter before you get there: seconds of hesitation will cost you your neck.

Do not throw grenades if you can post them, and always fight down a house rather than up. This may not always be possible, especially if preliminary bombardment has been heavy.

The second after the grenade has burst, you must be in the room fir at anything that could a threat. If you hesitate may give the enemy tin to recover or reoccupy room.

974

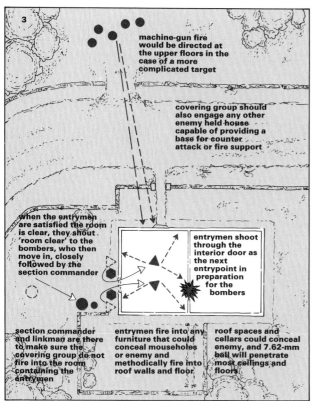

3 machine-gun fire would be directed at the upper floors in the case of a more complicated target

covering group should also engage any other enemy held house capable of providing a base for counter attack or fire support

when the entrymen are satisfied the room is clear, they shout 'room clear' to the bombers, who then move in, closely followed by the section commander

entrymen shoot through the interior door as the next entrypoint in preparation for the bombers

section commander and linkman are there to make sure the covering group do not fire into the room containing the entrymen

entrymen fire into any furniture that could conceal mouseholes or enemy and methodically fire into roof walls and floor

roof spaces and cellars could conceal enemy, and 7.62-mm ball will penetrate most ceilings and floors

As soon as the grenades burst, the entrymen get into the house. Back to back, they fire controlled bursts into the room and select the next entry point into the next room. Fire support is switched to the top floor and other rooms as the entrymen go in.

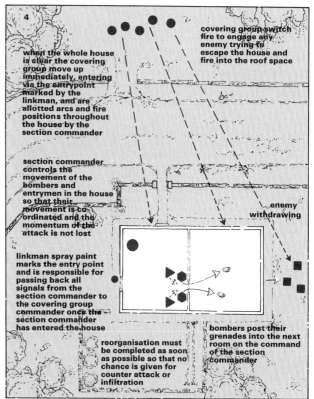

4 when the whole house is clear the covering group move up immediately, entering via the entrypoint marked by the linkman, and are allotted arcs and fire positions throughout the house by the section commander

covering group switch fire to engage any enemy trying to escape the house and fire into the roof space

section commander controls the movement of the bombers and entrymen in the house so that their movement is co-ordinated and the momentum of the attack is not lost

enemy withdrawing

linkman spray paint marks the entry point and is responsible for passing back all signals from the section commander to the covering group commander once the section commander has entered the house

reorganisation must be completed as soon as possible so that no chance is given for counter attack or infiltration

bombers post their grenades into the next room on the command of the section commander

The commander moves into the house to control the next attack. The linkman stays at the entry point to the house and relays orders from those inside. The bombers prepare their next grenades and move up to where the entrymen have kicked off the interior door.

follows:

1 Clearing Section. Their task will be to assault the house and clear it room by room in the same way as the bombers do for a section operation.

2 The Covering and Cut-Off Group. This could be just one section or possibly the remainder of the platoon.

3 The Reserve. If you need to use some of the covering and cut-off group as a back-up in the house, a reserve may be necessary, probably under the command of the platoon sergeant. The reserve takes over the business of covering and cut-off group, and also brings forward extra ammunition and evacuates casualties.

Whether you undertake house-clearing at section or platoon level, it is important that you keep to the drills outlined here. Use haphazard methods and you will cause unnecessary casualties. Powerful fire support, and careful planning can, however, overcome the most determined opposition.

But FIBUA is inevitably a very slow business. Your aim must be to remove the enemy with as few casualties as possible.

Without effective communications your fire support could cut through several rooms and start causing you casualties, so keep a tight grip of the gun teams and make sure they have visual contact with the link men at all times. Similarly, the link men must know where you have got to in the house you are clearing.

Combat Report
Djibouti:
Guerrilla Patrol

In 1983 I was serving with the 4th Squadron of the le Regiment Etranger de Cavalerie (REC) of the French Foreign Legion. We had been sent to Djibouti to replace the 2e Regiment Etranger de Parachutists (REP), who were on patrol in Chad.

It was September and my troop was on a long-range desert patrol. We'd been out for two weeks, so we were looking forward to returning to Arta for a decent meal, a bed, fresh water and a few ice-cold beers. On the last night we were about 50 miles from the Ethiopian border. The troop had settled down and I was standing guard by the radio truck, chatting to the signaller, when the radio started going mad. It was all in Morse code, but from what I could hear I knew we wouldn't be staying put for much longer.

The signaller told me to fetch our troop commander. When he got to the truck he took one look at the transcription and told me to wake the troops. We were moving out! After 10 minutes, and much swearing, the lads were ready.

We would be in trouble

The troop commander called us over and explained what was going on. There had been a clash on the border. Some guerrillas had come over into Djibouti, attacked a village and killed a few people. Our job was to try to capture them.

We drove off in different directions to begin the search. My battle group went straight to the village, arriving just as the sun was coming up. The villagers were very relieved to see us and immediately took us to their dead. There were three of them: two men and a woman. Each had been shot in the back of the head. Even at this hour they were beginning to smell, and there were flies everywhere.

We asked which way the guerrillas had gone, and were astounded to learn that they were only a couple of kilometres away. They were apparently under the impression that no-one would follow them, as it was very mountainous. We radioed the rest of the troop and told them we were going after the guerrillas.

Wearing Ray-Bans against the glaring heat of the Ethiopian border region, this Legionnaire is manning an AA-52 general-purpose machine-gun.

We drove about two kilometres, then got out and went up on to the ridgeline, where we immediately spotted a wisp of smoke. I thought we'd got them, but they were just below the next ridgeline, which would take quite a bit of time to get to as the hills were very steep. Also, if they saw us we would be in big trouble.

And that is exactly what happened. They saw us coming down off the first ridgeline and opened up. Although none of their rounds came near, I set up our machine-gun and started to put down some very effective covering fire: so effective that when we eventually got up on to the ridgeline we found a dead guerrilla.

The rest had done a bunk and were running like hell down the hill. We opened up on them, but the distance was too great and they were ducking and weaving in between the rocks and scrub.

"Get Down!"

As we started to follow, one of the guerrillas went down on one knee. At first I thought he'd been hit, but in fact he was taking aim with an RPG-7. Someone shouted, "Get down!" and I dived into some rocks, badly grazing my knees in the process. At least that was better than getting an RPG wrapped around my head.

Fortunately the rocket went over us, but the explosion dislodged a load of rocks which started rolling down the hill towards us. We had nowhere to run to, so I tucked my head under my arms and started praying. I was hit by a few small rocks and covered in dust, but apart from that I was OK.

As soon as everything had settled down I jumped up to see where the guerrillas had got to. I couldn't see anything, but I heard one of our group calling for help. He had fractured his leg just above the knee and was losing a lot of blood. I called for the medic, but he was unconscious. Another man was bruised, and we were all a bit shaken.

Now we had problems: we were stuck halfway up a hill with three injured men and only one stretcher, which was back in the truck, plus we didn't know where the guerrillas had got to. I was pretty sure, though, that they were still running, thinking that we were in hot pursuit.

Our sergeant radioed the troop commander and explained what had happened, saying that we needed a helicopter for the casualties. Then

A heavily-armed Panhard AML-90 armoured car on patrol through the desert.

a man was sent back to the truck to collect the stretcher so that we could move the injured to a place where the helicopter could land.

The rest of the troop were about an hour's drive away, so for the time being we were on our own. The sergeant checked the map and looked for a landing zone. There was a plateau about four miles away, so we had to carry the injured to the truck and drive there. It sounded so easy!

By now the sun was beating down and the heat was stifling. The only water we had was in our water bottles, and that was being used to keep the injured cool. When the guy returned with the stretcher we loaded up Quinnet, the medic, who was the most serious, and then four of us lifted him on to our shoulders and set off for the truck. Our sergeant and two others stayed with the two remaining injured.

Again it was sheer hell

Carrying the stretcher to the truck was painful. It took about 45 minutes. Once there, we put up a lean-to for Quinnet, to keep the sun off him. Then we had a drink from the water-trailer and refilled our flasks for the walk back to collect the next casualty. I told one of the Legionnaires to stay with Quinnet and to act as a guide for the rest of the troop when they arrived. Then off we went.

Getting back was no real hardship and we made good time. On this trip we picked up Lollierou, who had the open fracture. The two who had stayed behind with the sergeant changed places with two of us, and we set out once again for the truck.

Again it was sheer hell and Lollierou cried out every time we jarred the stretcher, which was almost every step, but there was nothing we could do. Luckily, after a kilometre we saw the rest of the troop coming over a hill. I have never been so relieved to see anyone. We just put down the stretcher and waited for them.

When they arrived, eight of them took Lollierou and headed off towards the trucks while the rest of us went to collect the others. Then I went with the sergeant and checked the area around the dead guerrilla. We collected his AK-47 and some papers he'd been carrying, marked the place on the map, and rejoined the rest of the troop.

The drive to the plateau was slow and difficult, but we were rewarded when we got there by the sight of a Puma helicopter. We loaded up the injured and then went back to the trucks and drove off towards Arta. We knew that we could be staying out for another night, and everyone was hoping that the radio would stay quiet. If it didn't, we were more than ready to respond: for now, though, we just wanted to get back to camp for a shower and a good night's sleep.

CLEARING THE STREETS

The techniques of successful house-clearing, street warfare and fighting in built-up areas (FIBUA) are vital to the modern infantryman. Should war break out in Europe, much of the land battle will be fought in West Germany, one of the continent's most heavily urbanised areas.

This section of the Combat Skills course tells you how to set about securing a street that's held by enemy forces and describes the British Army's drill for securing an entire village.

So far we have looked at FIBUA in general and at house-clearing in particular. The techniques of clearing a house give you the basis for larger and more complex FIBUA operations, namely clearing a street or a village. Clearing a group of buildings is, obviously, a combination of many smaller house-clearing operations.

Clearing a street

Assuming you are faced with clearing a typical, fairly wide, European street, you will probably need to use two platoons, one on each side of the road. The advance should be controlled by the company commander, who will probably keep his third platoon in reserve to deal with any unforeseen eventualities.

It is a good idea for the two platoons to 'leapfrog' down the street. In other words, one platoon moves slightly ahead of the other, so that it can fire straight across the street at any enemy whom the rear platoon is about to attempt to dislodge.

Within each platoon, sections can also support each other. Having captured one house, a section can turn it into a firm base. From this the following section can mount its attack on the next house. If possible, keep your sections within voice or hand signal range.

Take the dominant building

Holding each successive house as a platoon advances down a street can be a problem. It soaks up your manpower and, if the houses are not to be re-taken by the enemy, can continue to do so. The knack is to identify and

A rifleman fires a controlled burst at the withdrawing enemy as students on the platoon commanders' battle course at the School of Infantry in Warminster attempt to wrestle Imber village from the evil grip of the Demonstration Battalion.

Clearing a street involves exactly the same principles as clearing a house, but the problems of command and control are multiplied. You cannot afford to go looking for trouble like this. Look round the bottom of the wall, and don't do anything until your mates are ready to support you.

When the attacking platoons move forward the reserve platoons must immediately occupy what has been taken. If you want to hold on to something you will have to occupy it.

Above: A section commander indicates the next section objective to his covering group commander.

Left: The assault group equipped with aluminium ladders charges forward under the cover of a hail of supporting fire, from not just the rest of the platoon but also the company. The essence of street fighting is that only one element moves, with the maximum fire support suppressing the rest of the position, and you bite off only a small part of the objective at a time.

Bombing
Heavy bombing makes very difficult for the infa man who has to fight through the rubble, but objective can be bombe accurately immediately before the infantry go in detrimental effect on th enemy defence will ma worthwhile.

Shelling
Continual shelling will discourage the enemy from using the upper storeys of any buildings and will make movement round his depth positions costly. Heavy artillery could destroy his strongpoints.

Warrior
Warrior equipped with the 30-mm Rarden cannon is a considerable addition to the infantry's firepower. Six-round bursts of 30-mm APSE (armour piercing secondary effect) will certainly suppress the enemy.

Using tanks
Tanks can be used to great effect in street fighting, even if movement is limited. A dozen rounds of AP (armour piercing) followed by a dozen rounds of HE should have the desired effect on an enemy strongpoint. Tanks should be used singly or in small numbers and should always be adequately supported by infantry.

84mm MAW
While the weapon will not destroy an enemy strongpoint or blow a hole in it large enough for an entry point, it does have a considerable shock effect on the occupants and may kill or injure. HE ammo for bunker busting is not available in the British Army.

STORMING A STRONGPOINT

Taking a street is usually a task given to a company (three platoons). Once the company commander has been given his objective, he will set up the company command post in a house where he can maintain comms with his two leading platoons.

Day or night
It is possible for infantry to seize a limited objective in a town and completely clear it at night, contrary to popular belief. This is the best way to gain a foothold in a defended area: rush in there just after your artillery has lifted under cover of darkness.

Barricades
The only roads that will not be barricaded are those leading to pre-selected killing grounds. Barricades will be mined, booby trapped and covered by fire from above, in front and behind.

hold the dominating buildings in the street, so that you can cover the surrounding buildings with fire and isolate them. You can leave individual snipers to do this job, thus conserving your manpower.

Obviously, you'll find it more difficult to sanitise buildings at night, but Night Observation Devices (NODs) and Image Intensification (II) sights will help you solve the problem. However, it's unrealistic to expect lone snipers to gaze through II sights all night long. Twenty-four-hour coverage will clearly soak up much more manpower.

Clearing a village

This is even more complex. Although you can clear very small hamlets of four or five houses, or perhaps a farm complex, with a platoon, a larger village could soak up at least a company and more probably a battalion. Larger towns and cities could involve brigades or even divisions.

The potential of an urban area to impede, delay, complicate and frustrate your advance is enormous. To use modern military jargon, urban areas are 'force multipliers' for the defender. In other words, a few determined and properly equipped men can hold up a much larger force for a very long time.

If you have to clear a small and easily defined village, use the following drill:

1 You will need a cut-off group, to work its way to a position where it will be able to cut off the enemy's likely line of retreat. If you are part of this group, you should do all you can to get into position undetected. In a larger village or town this will not be easy.

2 You will need a second group to provide covering fire along the main

A gun team prepares to race across the gap to cross the street under cover of supporting fire from the assault sections in the flats to their front. Ideally you should avoid having to cross gaps by fighting from house to house on the same side of the street, with another platoon doing the same on the other side.

Flame warfare
This is a major deficiency in the British Army. The Soviets have always recognised the potential of flame weapons for this type of fighting, and have developed a range of weapon systems including a number of rocket propelled napalm canisters in addition to the more conventional flamethrowers. The deficiency is currently under review.

Locating the enemy
It will not be as easy as this. Street fighting is a deadly game of hide and seek: if you miss a cellar you could find yourself rapidly cut off and under contact from both sides.

Ammunition
You will use far more small-arms ammunition in street fighting than in any other type of operation. 6 × 30-round magazines or 5 × 20-round magazines are simply not enough: each man will have to carry extra magazines and loose ammo, and each platoon and company will have to carry its own reserve.

A firm base
Start your attack from a firm base: one that is defendable and where you are safe from counter-attack, and limit the objective to a key building which must be recce'd by the commander.

The company commander must be far enough forward to control the assaulting platoons and 'read' the battle. At the same time, he has to keep out of any firefights. He has two radio operators; one talks forward to the platoons, and one passes messages back to battalion.

CLEARING A STREET

Symbol	Meaning	Symbol	Meaning
▬	Infantry section of eight men	⌐⌐⌐	building held by friendly forces
△	Company headquarters		
○	Platoon headquarters	▭	building held by enemy forces
➡	direction of assault		
⋈	entry point		
→	suppressing fire		

street of the village. If you are part of this group, it's vital that you watch each building like a hawk. If you can take out some of the enemy before the assault group goes in, you will have made the task of your comrades far easier.

3 The assault group will clear the village. This will probably mean a house by house battle. If you are a member of the assault group, you must follow all the rules of house-clearing. However, even though you must clear each house, remember that you have to clear the village as quickly as possible. Your task is to drive the enemy into the open and into the field of fire of the cut-off group.

Points to watch

So much for the drills. You should bear various points in mind when clearing a village. First, the defenders may not necessarily be in the buildings. Gardens or rough ground may provide better, less obvious, cover. If the enemy does his job properly, he will distribute his forces both inside and outside the buildings.

Second, you will by now have realised the importance of grenades in FIBUA operations. But remember that there is a limit to the number of grenades men can carry.

US Army manuals tend to recom-

INFILTRATION

If you do not physically occupy everything you have liberated from the enemy, you could be in for a nasty surprise as the enemy filters back at night or through the sewers into areas thought to be clear.

mend the liberal use of grenades before entering every room. The reality is that grenades are both heavy to carry and consume a lot of space in ammunition pouches. There is a limit to the amount that you can carry, and resupply may be difficult.

If you throw a grenade into every

This is how an infantry company advancing two platoons up, one in reserve would take an enemy-held street. The company has just taken over as the point company and has established a firm base on both sides of the road across the street from the enemy-held area. 2 Platoon attacks first with one section, with the rest of the company providing fire support, suppressing all the enemy positions that could support the target buidling.

2 Platoon's assaulting section would only be responsible for two or three rooms, the remainder of the house being taken by the second section. As soon as the house is cleared they fire on depth targets and one platoon's objective.

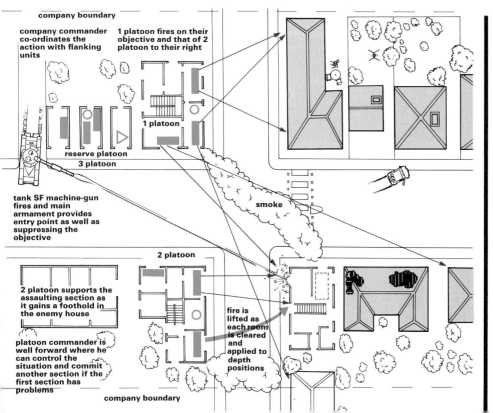

company boundary

company commander co-ordinates the action with flanking units

1 platoon fires on their objective and that of 2 platoon to their right

1 platoon

reserve platoon
3 platoon

tank SF machine-gun fires and main armament provides entry point as well as suppressing the objective

smoke

2 platoon

2 platoon supports the assaulting section as it gains a foothold in the enemy house

fire is lifted as each room is cleared and applied to depth positions

platoon commander is well forward where he can control the situation and commit another section if the first section has problems

company boundary

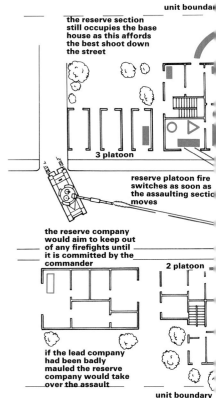

unit boundary

the reserve section still occupies the base house as this affords the best shoot down the street

3 platoon

reserve platoon fire switches as soon as the assaulting section moves

the reserve company would aim to keep out of any firefights until it is committed by the commander

2 platoon

if the lead company had been badly mauled the reserve company would take over the assault

unit boundary

The right way to deal with the problem: a burst of fire through the window to keep their heads down, then post them a grenade and go in with the rifle and bayonet.

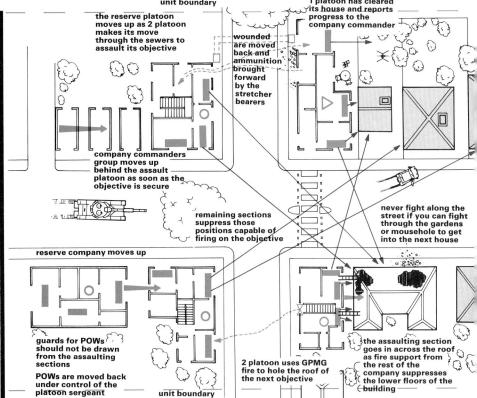

room you assault, you will soon exhaust your supply – and you may be embarrassed just when you need a grenade most. The British approach has always been to use ammunition more sparingly. It is a matter of battle discipline.

Third, you should shoot through all doors, ceilings or wooden partitions before dealing with anyone who may be beyond or above them. But this may not be enough. Remember when you enter a room to do so as quickly as you can, and put in a grenade first if you have enough available. If you haven't, you can usually coax someone out whose position is hopeless.

Expect the unexpected

You must look out for booby traps. If something looks like it needs moving, don't move it. Booby traps are relatively simple to construct and are ideal weapons for soldiers on the losing side. They can be initiated by completing an electrical circuit, by putting pressure on a device or, indeed, by releasing pressure from a device.

A GPMG gunner fires at the next platoon objective as the cover group for the section prepare to cross the street. The better way, if possible, would be to mousehole through even if it means some sledgehammer work to cut holes by hand. Remember, sweat saves blood.

When you have successfully taken out a house, pause a while. Do not rush around exploring every cupboard, drawer and floorboard. The Engineers are trained to detect and deal with booby traps, and you should leave the job to them.

When you have cleared a village you may need to put it in a state of defence and hold it. The next section on FIBUA will go into the business of defending a built-up area and creating a strong point.

With fire support from the rest of the company, one platoon moves through the sewer to cross the street to gain a foothold in the house. It is the corporals' battle at this stage to get in and clear the enemy out of a number of rooms in the house, according to his orders.

Now with a foothold on both sides of the street, the fire groups would take up positions on the top floors where they can cover the whole street. Again, only one unit in the company will move at a time, using assault ladders to cross onto the roof of the next building and fight down. If the section takes too many casualties, the reserve section takes over with the remainder providing fire support. If the platoon is in difficulty they stay put and the reserve platoon take over. The process continues house-by-house down the street.

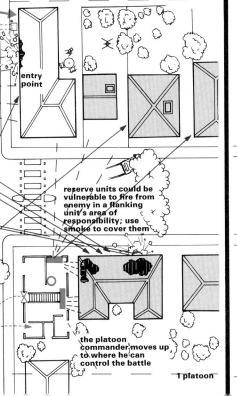

SUCKING CHEST WOUNDS

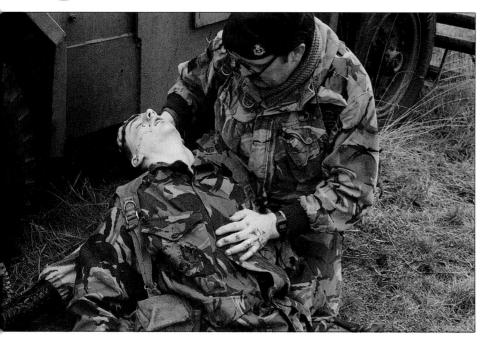

Above: A simulated sucking chest wound. Blood frothing at the mouth is a sign that air is being sucked into the chest cavity and the lung has collapsed.

Below: You need to make an airtight seal over the hole, so remove the casualty's clothing around the wound. In an NBC environment you must leave them on and do the best you can.

Chest injuries can be very serious and must be recognised and treated urgently; prompt evacuation to proper medical care is essential. You can treat superficial injuries like any other wound, with a clean dressing, but watch out for these serious problems.

Crush injuries

The casualty may have fractured ribs, often in several places. At the site of the injury the chest wall will no longer be rigid, and breathing becomes difficult as the chest is no longer effective in pumping air in and out of the lungs. Worse, air could be getting moved from one side of the chest and back again rather than up and down the windpipe. The casualty tries to overcome this by taking deeper breaths, which only makes matters worse.

Recognising the symptoms

Look for the following:

1 Abnormal movement of the chest
2 Painful and difficult breathing
3 Distress and anxiety
4 Cyanosis (blueness) of the lips and mouth
5 Signs of shock

Treatment

The aim of the treatment is to stop the abnormal movement of the chest wall. If the casualty is unconscious, you should:

1 Check and clear his airway
2 Place him in the three-quarters prone position
3 Place a hand over the injured area to provide support
4 Place a layer of padding over the area and secure it with a firm, broad bandage
5 Treat for shock
 If he is conscious, carry out steps 3 and 4 with him sitting upright.

Open chest wounds

If the wound is severe enough there may be a hole in the chest wall. Air will get in and the lung will collapse, and air will go in and out of the hole instead of up and down the windpipe.

Recognising the symptoms

Look for the following:

1 Shallow and difficult breathing
2 The sound of air being sucked in and out of the chest wall

3 Bloodstained fluid bubbling from the wound
4 Cyanosis of the lips and mouth
5 Signs of shock

Treatment

The aim is to prevent the air going in and out of the chest wall. Quite simply, you must plug the hole. Whether the casualty is conscious or unconscious, you should:

1 Make sure his airway is clear
2 Seal the hole in his chest by placing a large dressing over the wound and fixing it in place with a firm, broad bandage. Make sure it completely covers the wound, forming a seal.
3 Place the casualty on the injured side to help maintain the seal
4 Treat for shock

Bleeding into the chest

Crush or open wounds may be accompanied by bleeding into the chest. It may also happen without obvious external signs of injury, particularly following an explosion when the casualty suffers what is known as blast injury.

Recognising the signs

You should suspect bleeding into the chest if the casualty:

1 Shows signs of shock
2 Is coughing up blood
3 Has difficulty in breathing

Treatment

Unfortunately there is very little a first aider can do about internal bleeding into the chest apart from general measures for the treatment of shock. The important thing is to recognise that there is a problem and to arrange for urgent evacuation.

Get the casualty to exhale, then place the plastic-covered field dressing wrapper over the wound to seal it.

Above, right and below: tie a field dressing over the plastic wrapper. Maintain pressure over the wound as you wrap the tail of the dressing around and underneath the body. Tie the tails over the wound while the casualty breathes out.

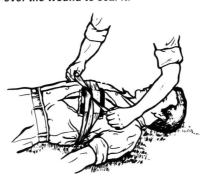

Right: A medic treats a wounded South Vietnamese Ranger during the fighting in Cholon during the Tet offensive in 1968. The Ranger was shot through the chest by a North Vietnamese sniper.

Below: Place the casualty on his injured side or sitting up, whichever makes it easier for him to breathe. Keep him warm and evacuate him as soon as possible.

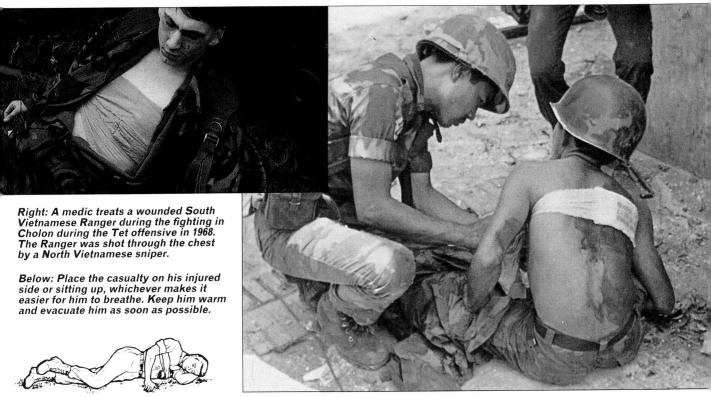

TREATING ABDOMINAL INJURIES

The wounds in these pictures are simulated.

WARNING
Casualties with abdominal wounds should not be given anything by mouth.

Above: Stomach wounds have often been fatal in past conflicts, and they are still among the most dangerous wounds you can suffer. Internal bleeding and infection from a torn gut is a deadly combination.

Below: Abdominal wounds often produce a horrific mess of protruding organs. Leave them where they are: do not touch them or try to push them back in. This would simply add to the casualty's problems.

The abdomen, the part of the body between the chest and the pelvis, is often mistakenly referred to as the stomach. The stomach is just one of the contents of the abdomen; other important organs are the bowels, liver, spleen, kidneys and bladder. An abdominal injury may result in severe shock and the majority of cases will require surgery. Without it, the casualty will often die.

As well as injury to internal organs there may be considerable internal bleeding. A further cause of trouble is infection, which is particularly likely if the gut is penetrated or torn.

First aid treatment is very simple. All you can do is make the patient comfortable and cover the wound.

Recognising the symptoms

An abdominal wound is usually obvious and part of the guts may be sticking out. There may be severe bruising to the abdomen or lower chest, back or groin. The injury may be the result of a direct blow, or the casualty may have suffered a blast injury. Other signs are:

1 Pain or tenderness in the abdomen
2 Vomiting, which may contain blood
3 Tense abdominal muscles
4 Shock

Left: Pick up any internal organs lying on the ground using a clean dressing and place them on top of the casualty's abdomen. Secure dressings in place with bandages, but do not apply them tightly: internal bleeding cannot be controlled with external pressure.

Below: Position the casualty on his back with his knees up to prevent further exposure of the bowel. Flex his knees to relax the abdominal muscles and any internal pressure.

Left: Settle the casualty on his back with knees drawn up. Keep him under close observation and turn his head to one side as he is likely to vomit.

Treatment

Make the casualty lie down on his back with his knees drawn up. This will help to relax the muscles and ease the strain on the abdomen. If the patient is not suffering too much shock, the head and shoulders may also be raised.

Cover the wound with a clean dressing. If any guts or tissues are sticking out, don't try to push them back in: just leave them as they are and cover with the dressing. Also, don't try to remove debris from the wound or you make matters worse.

Do not give the casualty any food or drink, but protect him from further injury and from wind and rain, and keep him warm. Arrange for speedy evacuation.

FIELD SANITATION

In war, the number of casualties due to enemy action has always been exceeded by the number caused by illness, and similar problems often arise on expeditions and military exercises. Very often this is due to bad hygiene leading to stomach upsets and diarrhoea.

You can avoid illness by taking proper preventive measures. You must be fit to start with, maintain personal hygiene, and change into clean clothes as often as possible. Pay attention to food and water, and dispose of waste carefully.

General health

Before setting out on any form of expedition or training you must be in good general health: if you are suffering from flu or a stomach upset, for example, these are likely to get worse. Also, if you are suffering from or just recovering from an infectious disease you may get worse yourself and will almost certainly pass it on to others.

Make sure your teeth and gums are in good condition. Many a soldier on operations or training has had to be evacuated because of dental trouble.

Personal hygiene

1 Keep as clean as possible, paying particular attention to your feet: these must be washed every day and dusted with powder.
2 Clean your teeth regularly.
3 Continue to shave every day, even though it's easier not to bother. But avoid after-shave, not just for practical reasons but because it will dry your skin and make it sore.
4 Change into clean clothes as often as possible, and change your socks every day. Natural fibres such as wool and cotton will breathe and allow sweat to evaporate. If you are out for any length of time you will have to wash your clothes: you can buy traveller's clothes-washing liquid in a tube, which will work in cold water.

Personal cleanliness is essential if a combat unit is to function properly. This does not just mean clean feet: dental problems can put you completely out of action, and a dirty mess tin is a good route to food poisoning.

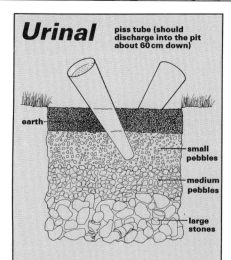

Urinal

piss tube (should discharge into the pit about 60 cm down)

earth—
—small pebbles
—medium pebbles
—large stones

Side view of a gravel pit with piss tubes drawn in. This sort of pit allows urine to drain quickly into the earth rather than create a foul-smelling swamp in camp. Place some obvious marker on the spot so you can find it at night.

Top view of a gravel pit: by arranging stones in order of their size you can create an efficient filter system. Water is allowed to run away into the earth while the stones trap larger bits of refuse.

Sickness and disease have usually been the cause of the majority of casualties in war. Large numbers of people living under canvas away from sanitation facilities can lead to serious health problems unless the correct procedures are followed. Poor sanitary arrangements can easily lead to typhoid, cholera and a host of other diseases.

Lazyman boiler

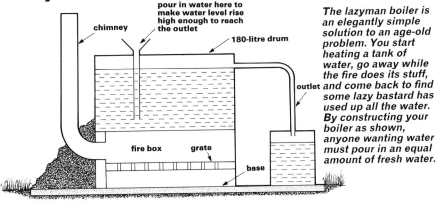

The lazyman boiler is an elegantly simple solution to an age-old problem. You start heating a tank of water, go away while the fire does its stuff, and come back to find some lazy bastard has used up all the water. By constructing your boiler as shown, anyone wanting water must pour in an equal amount of fresh water.

Labels in diagram: chimney; pour in water here to make water level rise high enough to reach the outlet; 180-litre drum; outlet; fire box; grate; base

Water

In Britain you can drink tap water, but this is not necessarily the case in the rest of the world. Even in Europe, although most indoor taps are safe, those in farmyards may not be.

Never assume that river or stream water is safe, even if it looks clear. Any water that you cannot be sure about must be purified by boiling or by adding water purification tablets. These will be on issue, or you can buy them from camping shops.

All water that is used for drinking and cooking should be treated. It is not necessary to purify water for washing, but avoid it if it's obviously polluted.

Field latrines

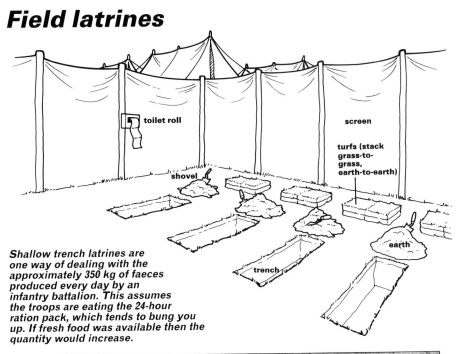

Labels: toilet roll; screen; turfs (stack grass-to-grass, earth-to-earth); shovel; trench; earth

Shallow trench latrines are one way of dealing with the approximately 350 kg of faeces produced every day by an infantry battalion. This assumes the troops are eating the 24-hour ration pack, which tends to bung you up. If fresh food was available then the quantity would increase.

Food

Army compo food is in tins and can be eaten cold if necessary. The disadvantage is that it is heavy. Dehydrated food is light, but needs water and cooking. Fresh food tastes much better and is less boring, but needs to be looked after properly. Most of the time, you will live on a mixture of the various types. When using fresh food:

1 Keep meat, milk etc only for a short time
2 Keep it covered
3 Wash vegetables before eating them
4 If in doubt about its freshness, don't eat it

Sanitation

Stomach problems are often caused by failing to keep waste matter away from food. Washing and lavatory areas should be kept well away from the cooking area, and this must be clean and tidy. Dispose of all scraps immediately and wash up pots, pans and plates after every meal.

Right: The 5- or 6-metre deep, water-filled medieval-style pit. This works fine until some idiot pours disinfectant in, killing the bacteria that make the pit work.

Up Front with the VAB

The Renault VAB owes its development to the French insistence on relying as far as possible on the domestic market for the production of her military hardware. In the late 1960s the French army decided to issue its infantry units with both tracked and wheeled vehicles. Although tracked vehicles were obviously far stronger they were considerably more expensive to build, and required considerably more maintenance. It was thought wasteful to issue tracked vehicles to rear or support troops who were not tasked with meeting the enemy in head-on battle.

The French decided not to buy foreign equipment, although at the time there were several excellent armoured personnel carriers available within NATO. Development of the tracked AMX-10P MICV was already under way when in 1970 requirements for a wheeled "Forward Area" Armoured Vehicle was announced.

Prototypes of 4×4 and 6×6 vehicles built by Panhard and Saviem/Renault were tested extensively by the army, and in May 1974 the Saviem/Renault Group 4×4 VAB was selected. The prototype was so good that prepro-

duction vehicles were dispensed with, and the first production vehicle entered service in autumn 1976.

The French army required between 4,000 and 5,000 VABs. In June 1981 Renault announced that it had built 1,500 vehicles for the home and domestic markets and had orders for a further 5,000 assorted vehicles, which were being constructed at the rate of 50 per month.

According to figures published

Above: The VCI version is fitted with a one-man turret armed with a 20-mm cannon and co-axial 7.62-mm machine-gun. It carries up to nine fully-equipped infantrymen in the troop compartment.

Below: Capable of over 90 km/h and with ranges of 1100-1300 km, the VAB series is highly mobile. Independently suspended wheels with large clearance help VABs cope with 60 per cent gradients and 30 per cent slopes.

annually by the International Institute for Strategic Studies, by 1st July 1987 France had taken delivery of 2,540 4×4 VABs and 60 anti-tank variants. She is expected to order the more complex 6×6 version, which has been exported successfully to many of her allies, particularly Morocco.

Construction

The basic model in service with the French army is the 4×4 VAB VTT,

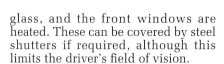

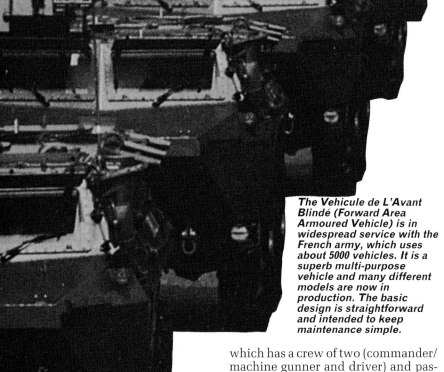

The Vehicule de L'Avant Blindé (Forward Area Armoured Vehicle) is in widespread service with the French army, which uses about 5000 vehicles. It is a superb multi-purpose vehicle and many different models are now in production. The basic design is straightforward and intended to keep maintenance simple.

which has a crew of two (commander/ machine gunner and driver) and passenger compartment for a section of 10 infantrymen. The 5.98-metre long all-welded steel hull provides protection from small arms fire and shell splinters, but would be of little use against concentrated heavy artillery bombardment or enemy tanks.

The driver sits to the front left of the vehicle with the commander/ machine gunner to his right. Both crewmen have small forward opening doors for easy access. The front and door windows contain bullet-proof

glass, and the front windows are heated. These can be covered by steel shutters if required, although this limits the driver's field of vision.

In its basic form the 4×4 VAB VTT is fitted with front opening hatches above both crew positions, but all French models have had a small Creusot-Loire rotating gun mount fitted above the commander's seat. Early models were armed with a 7.62-mm machine-gun capable of 360 degree traverse and an elevation of −15 to +45 degrees conventionally and from −20 to +80 degrees in the anti-aircraft mode, but current models are now fitted with a 12.7-mm (0.5-in) Browning M2 HB heavy machine-gun.

Browning machine-gun

Despite its age (it first entered service with the United States Army in 1933), the M2 HB is a thoroughly reliable and potent weapon. Fed by a 110-round disintegrating metal-link belt and with a cyclic rate of 450 to 550 rounds per minute, it would be effective against lightly armoured enemy reconnaissance vehicles that might be found behind the front line but would not penetrate the armoured protection of tanks or MICVs.

A passageway on the right side of the hull connects the crew compartment with the passengers seated in the rear. The infantrymen enter and leave the vehicle via two outward-opening rear doors, each of which has a window that can be covered by an armoured shutter.

Three firing ports are provided on each side of the hull. Although these

VABs are amphibious, propelled in the water by hydrojets at 7.2 km/h. Before entering the water you must switch on the bilge pumps and raise the trim vane on the glacis plate. You steer the waterjets using a joystick on the dashboard.

Inside the VAB

Both the 4×4 and 6×6 versions of the VAB have the same general structure. The hull is sufficiently armoured to protect the occupants from small arms fire, grenades and shell fragments. All are amphibious, and NBC systems, heating, de-frosting, and air-conditioning are all available, depending on the customer's requirements. This is a VPM 120 in a desert camouflage developed for models exported to the Middle East.

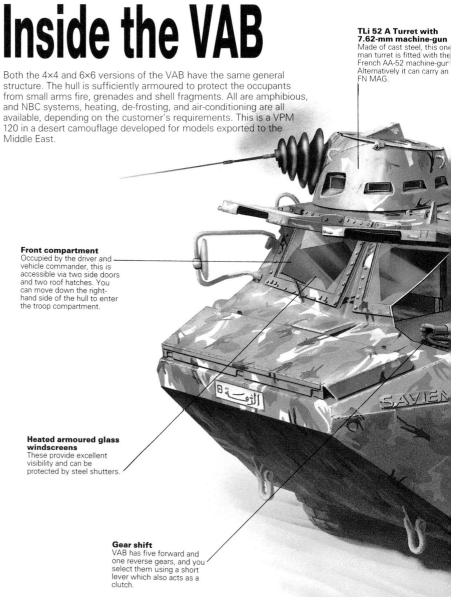

TLi 52 A Turret with 7.62-mm machine-gun
Made of cast steel, this one-man turret is fitted with the French AA-52 machine-gun. Alternatively it can carry an FN MAG.

Front compartment
Occupied by the driver and vehicle commander, this is accessible via two side doors and two roof hatches. You can move down the right-hand side of the hull to enter the troop compartment.

Heated armoured glass windscreens
These provide excellent visibility and can be protected by steel shutters.

Gear shift
VAB has five forward and one reverse gears, and you select them using a short lever which also acts as a clutch.

can be secured open externally to enable the passengers to fire their small arms on the move, the soldiers are seated on benches running along both sides of the hull (as opposed to back-to-back, facing outwards, as in the case of the Soviet BMP), so accurate marksmanship is virtually impossible. A circular hatch, to which a variety of armament installations can be fitted, is situated above the forward part of the upper hull, with two smaller hatches, opening forward, to its rear.

The troop compartment is spacious, to reduce troop discomfort as far as possible: particularly important when you remember that reinforcements, many of whom will spend a considerable time travelling, will have to be fit and fresh when delivered to the battlefield. If necessary the seats can be folded to enable up to 2,000 kg of cargo to be carried.

Powerpack

The engine, transmission and 300-litre fuel tank are situated together behind the driver and offset to the left, enabling the crew access to the crew compartment. French models are fitted with a MAN D 2356 HM 72 six-cylinder inline water-cooled diesel developing 235 hp at 2200 rpm, but since 1984 this has been replaced in export models with the Renault VI MIDS 06.20.45 six-cylinder inline water-cooled turbo-charged diesel engine, developing 230 hp at 2200 rpm.

Power is transmitted to the wheels by a hydraulic torque converter and transmission with five forward and one reverse gears, and a small pneumatically-operated lever operates both the gears and clutch. The wheels

A VAB undergoes a fire test. Quiet and relatively unobtrusive, it makes a good IS (Internal Security) vehicle. Note that the armoured shutters have been lowered to protect the windscreen.

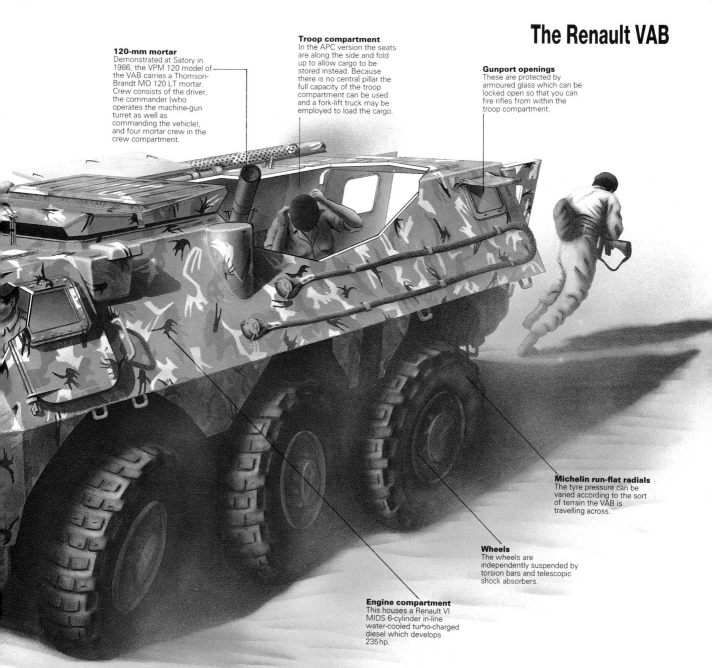

120-mm mortar
Demonstrated at Satory in 1986, the VPM 120 model of the VAB carries a Thomson-Brandt MO 120 LT mortar. Crew consists of the driver, the commander (who operates the machine-gun turret as well as commanding the vehicle), and four mortar crew in the crew compartment.

Troop compartment
In the APC version the seats are along the side and fold up to allow cargo to be stored instead. Because there is no central pillar the full capacity of the troop compartment can be used and a fork-lift truck may be employed to load the cargo.

Gunport openings
These are protected by armoured glass which can be locked open so that you can fire rifles from within the troop compartment.

Michelin run-flat radials
The tyre pressure can be varied according to the sort of terrain the VAB is travelling across.

Wheels
The wheels are independently suspended by torsion bars and telescopic shock absorbers.

Engine compartment
This houses a Renault VI MIDS 6-cylinder in-line water-cooled turbo-charged diesel which develops 235 hp.

are independently suspended by torsion bars and hydraulic shock absorbers. All wheels are run-flat with pressure controlled internally, and in the case of the front pair (front four in the case of the 6×6) are hydraulically assisted.

The versatile VAB is capable of a top speed of 92 km/h, has an excellent road range of 1,000 km, can climb gradients of 60 per cent and will be an ideal way of getting reinforcements and supplies to France's forward divisions based in West Germany.

Amphibious properties

With the exception of a few early French army models, VABs are fully amphibious and capable of a maximum water speed of 7 km/h. Propulsion comes from two Dowty water jets fitted to the rear of the hull. Both jets

are fitted with a deflector for steering and reverse thrust and are hydraulically controlled by a small joystick mounted on the dashboard.

Before entering the water, bilge pumps are switched on, and the trim vane, which at all other times is folded back on the glacis plate, is erected on the front of the boat-shaped hull.

With their usual eye on the Third World export market, the French have designed the basic VAB as little more than a relatively cheap shell to which a series of extras can be added when finances permit. Optional equipment includes an NBC system (fitted to all French army models), infra-red or passive night vision equipment, an air conditioning system, gas dispensers and grenade throwers. A front-mounted winch with a capacity of 7,000 kg, doubled with the aid of a

The French army uses the VCAC anti-tank version, which is a 4×4 model of the VAB fitted with the Euromissile Mephisto system. It has four ready-to-fire HOT missiles and the launcher can be retracted when not in use so the vehicle looks like an ordinary APC.

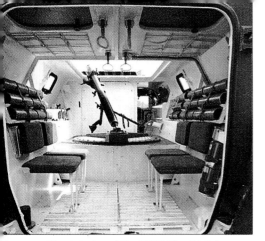

The interior of the VPM 81, which has an 81-mm mortar fitted on a turntable with 360° traverse and has a range of 5 km. The VPM 120 is similar, carrying a Thomson-Brandt 120-mm mortar with a range of 7 km and much more powerful ammunition.

pulley, and 60 metres of cable can be fitted to give the vehicle a basic engineering capability.

Variants

The spacious VAB can easily be adapted. Although never intended as a front-line combat vehicle, a VCI Infantry Combat Vehicle (Vehicule de Combat de L'Infantrie) has been developed for export and for use by the French air force for air field defence. Manned by a crew of three (commander, driver and gunner) and capable of carrying eight fully-equipped infantrymen, the VCI is armed with a centrally-mounted 20-mm cannon and 7.62-mm co-axial machine-gun.

Approximately 60 VAB HOT anti-tank vehicles carrying the Euromissile Mephisto system with four ready-to-launch HOT missiles are in French service, and a similar system fitted with a UTM turret has been exported to Qatar. Capable of destroying any APC and all but the latest generation of tanks, the HOT missile with its maximum range of 4,000 metres remains a formidable weapon.

Two mortar vehicles have appeared: the VTM (Vehicule Tracteur de Mortier), which tows a Brandt 120-mm mortar, and a prototype which fires an 81-mm mortar through a two-part opening in the roof. Command, artillery control and surveil-

Battlefield Evaluation: comparing

VAB

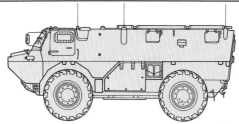

Specification: (6×6 version)
Crew: 2+10
Combat weight: 14.2 tonnes
Road speed: 92 km/h
Power to weight ratio: 16.5 hp/tonne
Length: 5.98 m
Height: 2.06 m
Armament: variable

Assessment
Firepower	***
Protection	***
Age	**
Worldwide users	**

The VAB is a versatile combat vehicle. A highly successful APC, it can carry HOT anti-tank missiles and operate as a tank destroyer with four missiles ready to fire. It can serve as an ambulance, command post or internal security vehicle. In the French army, one major role is to carry MILAN anti-tank guided missile teams. Oman has bought 20 VABs with twin 20-mm anti-aircraft guns and the French army's anti-aircraft VAB will have MATRA SATCP missiles. Renault have also demonstrated a VAB fitted with a Brandt 120-mm mortar.

A VAB is a highly versatile combat vehicle. This is the VCI model, fitted with a TL20S 20-mm turret.

SIBMAS

Specification:
Crew: 3+11
Combat weight: 14.5 to 16.5 tonnes depending on role
Road speed: 100 km/h
Power to weight ratio: 19.4 hp/tonne
Length: 7.32 m
Height: 2.24 m
Armament: various

Assessment
Firepower	***
Protection	***
Age	**
Worldwide users	*

The SIBMAS is a useful APC or weapons carrier produced as a private venture by a Belgian company. Malaysia spent £50 million to buy 162 Armoured Fire Support Vehicles (armed with a Cockerill 90-mm gun) plus 24 Armoured Recovery Vehicle versions. The SIBMAS follows the same pattern as the VAB: a standard hull with sufficient armour to withstand 7.62-mm armour-piercing rounds and a wide choice of weapons fits. It can operate as an APC or carry anti-aircraft guns, a 90-mm gun, a 60-mm mortar and co-axial 20-mm cannon or various cannon and machine-gun fits.

SIBMAS is a privately-manufactured APC, produced in Belgium and purchased by Malaysia.

Vickers Valkyr

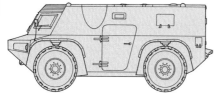

Specification:
Crew: 2+10
Combat weight: 11 tonnes
Road speed: 100 km/h
Power to weight ratio: 16.36 hp/tonne
Length: 5.6 m
Height: 2.05 m
Armament: various

Assessment
Firepower	***
Protection	***
Age	*
Worldwide users	—

The Vickers Valkyr armoured personnel carrier is another multi-purpose wheeled combat vehicle. Offered for sale by Vickers Defence Systems, it has yet to win an order, but follows the same pattern as the VAB. The armoured glass windscreen and vision blocks are proof against shell splinters, the front hull will withstand 7.62-mm AP rounds, and the rest of the hull is proof against point-blank 7.62-mm rounds. Armament fits include 7.62-mm or 12.7-mm machine-guns; 20-mm cannon plus 60-mm mortar; 90-mm gun or twin 20-mm anti-aircraft guns.

The Vickers Valkyr is similar to the VAB; a capable APC and IS vehicle with varied weaponry.

lance radar variants complete the series so far.

The VAB is without doubt one of the greatest success stories of French military design. Construction will continue for many years to come, and new variants will no doubt continue to come onto the export market, The VAB is cheap and easy to produce and simple to maintain and drive, and can fulfil most non-combatant roles.

The VAB ambulance is designed to provide rapid aid to wounded men directly on the battlefield. It can carry either four stretcher cases, 10 sitting wounded or two stretcher cases and five sitting wounded. It has a ventilation system for greater comfort.

the VAB with its rivals

Saracen

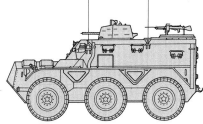

Replaced by the FV 432 as the British Army's APC in the early 1960s, some Saracens are still retained for Internal Security operations. Comparison with the VAB shows how far APC design has moved in the last 30 years. Saracen has no NBC system, is not amphibious and is built to take a one-man turret fitted with a machine-gun. However, the large numbers of Saracens supplied to armies all over the world has led to modernisation kits being offered by several companies.

Specification:
Crew: 2+10
Combat weight: 10.1 tonnes
Road speed: 72 km/h
Power to weight ratio: 15.73 hp/tonne
Length: 5.23 m
Height: 2 m
Armament: 1×7.62 mm machine gun

Assessment
Firepower ★
Protection ★★★
Age ★★★★★
Worldwide users ★★★★

The Saracen appeared in the 1950s and has been supplied to many armies, especially in Africa.

Panhard VCR

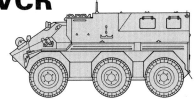

The Panhard VCR has been sold to several countries, including the UAE and Iraq. A conventional 6×6 APC, it has a 'V' shaped hull to minimise damage from mines and, following the Panhard tradition, the middle pair of wheels can be raised off the ground for speedy road travel. Only the front wheels are steered, and the low-pressure tyres enable it to travel 100 km after they have been punctured by bullets if you keep your speed below 30 km/h. Armament fits are as diverse as those of the VAB and include twin ready-to-launch MILAN missiles.

Specification: (APC)
Crew: 3+9
Combat weight: 7.9 tonnes
Road speed: 100 km/h
Power to weight ratio: 19.6 hp/tonne
Length: 4.87 m
Height: 2.13 m
Armament: various

Assessment
Firepower ★★★
Protection ★★★
Age ★★
Worldwide users ★★★

The Panhard VCR series of APCs have exported to several armies in the Middle East.

Saxon

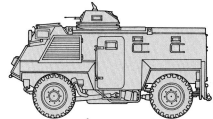

The British Saxon APC has been adopted by various armies in the Middle East as well as Nigeria and Malaysia. A tough and versatile vehicle, the Saxon may not have much aesthetic appeal but will play an increasingly important role in the British Army, carrying UK-based BAOR reinforcement brigades. It will carry a MILAN team or 81-mm mortar and can be used as a recovery vehicle.

Specification:
Crew: 2+10
Combat weight: 10.67 tonnes
Road speed: 96 km/h
Power to weight ratio: 13.68 hp/tonne
Length: 5.1 m
Height: 2.6 m
Armament: various

Assessment
Firepower ★★
Protection ★★★
Age ★★
Worldwide users ★★★

Saxon is the new British wheeled APC. It can carry a MILAN team or mortar.

Tornado: Low Level Penetrator

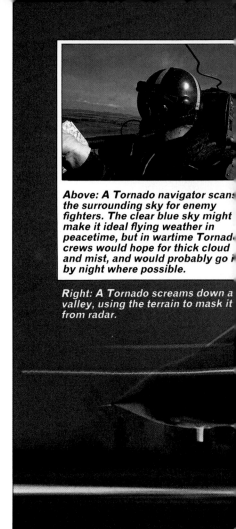

Above: A Tornado navigator scans the surrounding sky for enemy fighters. The clear blue sky might make it ideal flying weather in peacetime, but in wartime Tornado crews would hope for thick cloud and mist, and would probably go in by night where possible.

Right: A Tornado screams down a valley, using the terrain to mask it from radar.

NATO's air forces would have a crucial role to play in any future European conflict. The sorties flown by NATO offensive aircraft can be divided into four distinct types of mission: close air support, battlefield air interdiction, long-range interdiction, and offensive, counter-air operations.

Close Air Support over the battlefield would mainly be the responsibility of the RAF's Harriers, USAF A-10s, and West German Alpha Jets, operating between the FLOT (Forward Line of Troops) and the Fire Support Co-ordination Line.

The latter is established by the ground commander as the area in which he can co-ordinate assets not under his immediate control, such as long-range artillery and ground attack aircraft, against directly engaged enemy forces. Enemy forces further

back, and not yet directly engaged, would be attacked by the same aircraft, and by aircraft such as the F-16.

Such attacks, aimed at isolating the enemy from his reinforcements, disrupting his resupply operations and restricting his freedom of manoeuvre, are known as Battlefield Air Interdiction sorties.

NATO's force of Panavia Tornados, flown by the Italian air force, the Federal German Luftwaffe and Britain's Royal Air Force, could be tasked with any of these types of mission, although they are optimised for long-range interdiction and offensive counter air missions, flying against

With a Marconi Sky Shadow ECM pod outboard under the port wing, this Tornado GR.Mk 1 is seen transiting through friendly territory at high level to conserve fuel. To penetrate hostile airspace it will descend to treetop height.

targets much further beyond the FLOT. The purpose of interdiction missions is to destroy, neutralise or delay the enemy's military strength while it is still far enough away for co-ordination with other friendly fire to be unnecessary. Where the aim is to destroy enemy air power by destroying airfields, fuel or ammunition stores, or communications facilities, the term 'Offensive Counter Air' is used.

Heavy defences

Such targets are usually located deep within enemy territory, and the Tornado pilot will often have to penetrate heavy defences. In order to ensure the best chance of success the Tornado is equipped to make the maximum use of terrain and bad weather to approach the target undetected, and to deliver its weapons with deadly precision. Terrain-following radar allows the Tornado to automatically 'hug the contours' in all weathers, slipping under enemy radar and making maximum use of terrain masking.

A sophisticated attack radar and a highly accurate inertial navigation system allow the crew to find and attack any target with pinpoint accu-

Afterburners blazing, all lights on, this RAF Tornado GR.Mk 1 blasts off into the night for a low-level attack sortie. No other aircraft in the world can match the Tornado's ability to accurately deliver its warload with pinpoint accuracy, whatever the weather.

racy, in all weathers, at any time of day. Changes of flightplan to avoid threats, or to take account of changing circumstances, are always possible, with no effect on accurate navigation. The highly accurate navigation system and on-board computer make weapons delivery very accurate.

Survivability of the Tornado is improved by taking advantage of foul weather or night time, when many enemy fighters are ineffective, and is further enhanced by a comprehensive ECM (Electronic Counter-Measures) system. Well-trained, highly skilled aircrew use soundly conceived and effective tactics to further improve the performance of the aircraft.

The Tornado can drop a wide range of weapons on its targets, from 'dumb' iron bombs to specialised weapons including cluster bombs, anti-radar missiles, and even nuclear weapons. Built-in 27-mm Mauser cannon can be used for strafe attacks against targets of opportunity, or for self defence against enemy aircraft. AIM-9L Side-

Tornado interdiction mission

Interdiction is the term used to describe deep strike missions intended to destroy, neutralise or delay the enemy's military potential before it can be brought to bear, and undertaken sufficiently far beyond the FLOT (Forward Line of Troops) that detailed planning to ensure integration with friendly fire is not necessary.

1 A request for a Tornado mission reaches the squadron in the form of an Air Task Message, giving details of the target and the type of attack required. Aircrews plan their routes and tactics quickly and efficiently.

2 Tornado aircrew would probably have to fly in cumbersome NBC protective clothing, carrying portable ventilator units until they can 'plug into' the aircraft's oxygen system.

3 After passing through an elaborate system of air locks, the crews are driven to their respective Hardened Aircraft Shelters in armoured vehicles, protected by armed guards against Spetsnaz attack.

Weapons and Equipment Guide

winders can be carried if the air threat is expected to be significant.

NATO's Tornado squadrons are all housed in hardened accommodation and could continue to operate normally even in conditions of heavy NBC contamination. An RAF Tornado mission would be mounted in response to an ATM (Air Task Message) from an ATOC (Air Tasking Operations Centre).

Station Operations Centre

This would give specific details concerning the nature of the target and the aims of the requested sortie, including the required time on target. It would be passed directly to the Station Operations Centre, who would assess the priority of the target and determine whether the task could be fulfilled taking into account aircraft availability and time on target. If the decision is positive the task is passed to a squadron, who immediately begin planning the mission.

The number of aircraft involved and the amount and nature of ordnance to be 'delivered' will often be specified in the ATM, so planning concentrates on the details of the sortie, including the route to the target, the best direction to attack from, and tactics to be used by the formation over the target and on the ingress and egress. One of the squadron's Flight Commander's war role would be to act as full-time 'War Exec' or 'Warlord', who would be responsible for deciding how best a task could be implemented, and for allocating crews and aircraft. He would also be responsible for running the squadron site on a day-to-day basis, assisted by an operations ser-

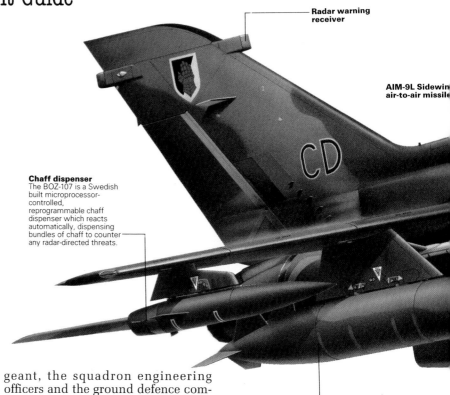

Radar warning receiver

AIM-9L Sidewinder air-to-air missile

Chaff dispenser
The BOZ-107 is a Swedish built microprocessor-controlled, reprogrammable chaff dispenser which reacts automatically, dispensing bundles of chaff to counter any radar-directed threats.

geant, the squadron engineering officers and the ground defence commander.

'Roving Auth'

A copy of the Air Task Message is passed to the authorising officer, known as the 'Roving Auth', who will find the designated formation leader and his navigator and brief them. Another copy of the ATM will be given to the Ground Liaison Officer, an army officer permanently attached to the squadron who looks after target intelligence and co-ordination of routes with 'friendly' artillery fire.

Relevant 1:500 000, or 'half mil' maps are selected, and the route, turning points and targets plotted. Larger

External fuel tank
The Tornado can carry up to four 1500-litre fuel tanks on its inboard underwing and underfuselage hardpoints, dramatically extending its range.

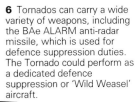

SG.357 parachute-retarded runway-cratering, shaped-charge bomblet

---

4 The Tornado cannot taxi or take off from grass, but its phenomenal performance allows it to take off from short strips of concrete, perhaps on undamaged stretches of a cratered runway or on a taxiway.

5 UK-based Tornados would refuel in flight from Victor or VC10 tankers while transiting at high level across the North Sea. This conserves fuel and extends range. Closer in to the target, the aircraft will descend to ultra low level, aiming to sneak in under the enemy radar.

6 Tornados can carry a wide variety of weapons, including the BAe ALARM anti-radar missile, which is used for defence suppression duties. The Tornado could perform as a dedicated defence suppression or 'Wild Weasel' aircraft.

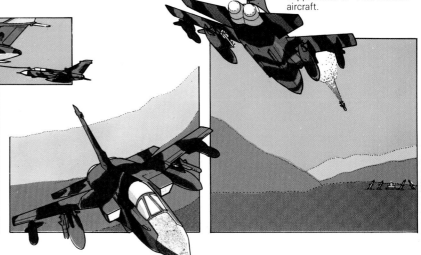

Inside the Tornado

Navigator
Probably more accurately termed a weapons systems officer, the backseater is reponsible for managing the weapons system and operating the radar, as well as for actually navigating the aircraft.

Pilot
Both pilot and navigator sit on Martin Baker Mk 10A zero-zero ejection seats.

UHF aerials

Radome
The radome covers the scanners for the Texas Instruments multi-mode ground mapping radar, and beneath it for the terrain-following radar.

UHF/Tacan aerial

Laser rangefinder and marked target seeker
This small device can fire a laser beam at the ground ahead of the aircraft, analysing the reflected laser energy to determine slant-range. It can also detect reflected laser energy from targets 'illuminated' by laser designators carried by troops or other aircraft.

Gun
Tornado is armed with two 27-mm Mauser cannon, each with 180 rounds of ammunition.

HB.876 self-righting area denial mine

JP233 airfield attack weapon

scale Ordnance Survey maps are used to plot the run from the Initial Point to the target. Timing marks and planned fuel states are also marked on the maps, which are taken into the air in case the Tornado's highly sophisticated navigation system goes unserviceable. Once the maps are complete, the navigator loads all the navigational information into the Cassette Preparation Ground Station (CPGS). He adds the geographical co-ordinates of the aircraft's HAS and the runway threshold, which allows the inertial navigation system to be aligned with phenomenal accuracy right at the

beginning of the sortie.

The navigator places his map on the electronic map table of the CPGS and 'aligns' it by placing a cursor over any two grid intersections and typing in the co-ordinates. He then places the cursor over each turning point, which are automatically translated into latitudes and longitudes, with times, and the flight plan is recorded on a cassette tape. A 'hard copy' on paper is also printed out.

When planning is complete, the crew kit-up for the flight, donning cumbersome NBC suits and respirators before being driven to the

7 One of the most effective weapons carried by the Tornado is the Hunting JP233 airfield attack weapon, which dispenses hundreds of runway cratering and area denial bomblets and mines. Built-in cannon are useful for strafing targets of opportunity.

8 If attacked by enemy fighters, the Tornado can defend itself using its cannon or AIM-9L Sidewinder air-to-air missiles. The best defence, however, lies in avoiding enemy fighters.

9 The Tornado's thrust reversers deploy automatically on landing, making it possible for the aircraft to use very short stretches of concrete. The Tornado can be quickly re-armed and refuelled for another trip.

Hardened Aircraft Shelter by armoured car. While the pilot checks the aircraft the navigator straps in, switches on the INS, and 'warms up' the radar. The engines are started and the aircraft swiftly taxi to the runway.

Card formation

The Tornados take off rapidly, using full afterburner to minimise the take-off distance, before forming up into a loose 'card' formation. To penetrate hostile airspace the Tornado will fly at very high speed and ultra-low level, the swept wing and fly-by-wire control system letting the aircraft 'ride out' the bumps and turbulence. A sophisticated terrain-following radar

allows the aircraft to fly at low level at night or in foul weather, automatically avoiding hills and ridges. It is an unnerving experience at first, sitting back and letting the aircraft lift you over the hills and down into the valleys. Radar is also used for navigation: a single sweep of the radar being used to find masts, to confirm that the aircraft is still on track, and to update the navigation system.

Attack choice

Targets can be attacked automatically, or manually. Some types of weapon can be tossed, or 'lofted' at the target without overflying it, while other's weapons require a laydown

An RAF Germany based Tornado taxis out from its Hardened Aircraft Shelter, built to withstand anything up to a direct hit by a 1,000-lb bomb. The squadron's HAS complex is well screened by trees to hide it from enemy aircraft.

Battlefield Evaluation: comparing

Tornado GR.Mk I

The Tornado was designed from the outset to replace the RAF's Buccaneers, Jaguars and even Vulcans in the tactical strike and interdiction roles. The aircraft relies heavily on its advanced radar and avionics to fly at high speed and at ultra low level in all weathers, minimising the chances of detection by hostile defences. The aircraft can deliver a wide range of weapons, nuclear or conventional, with pinpoint accuracy.

Specification:
Length overall: 16.72m
Wingspan: (fully spread) 13.91m
Maximum speed at sea level: 800 knots
Combat radius hi-lo-hi: 1390km
Maximum weapon load: 9,000kg
Take-off distance: 885m

Assessment
Manoeuvrability	****
Rough-field capability	***
Robustness	****
Range	****

Almost 1,000 Tornados have been ordered, for the air forces and a navy, of five countries.

Jaguar GR.Mk 1A

The Jaguar remains an extremely important low-level attack aircraft, in service with a number of air forces throughout the world and still in large-scale use in France and Britain. The single-seat Jaguar is capable of extremely accurate bombing, but lacks the blind, first pass, all-weather capability of the two-man Tornado.

Specification:
Length overall: 10.83m
Wingspan: 8.69m
Maximum speed at sea level: 729 knots
Combat radius hi-lo-hi: 1408km
Maximum weapon load: 4,763kg
Take-off distance: 565m

Assessment
Manoeuvrability	***
Rough-field capability	*****
Robustness	***
Range	****

The Jaguar remains a front-line strike aircraft in Britain and France, and has a host of export customers.

Dynamics F-111

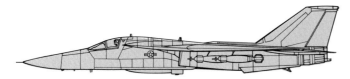

The General Dynamics F-111, first used operationally in Vietnam and more recently to bomb targets in Libya, remains an important and potent part of the USAF's deterrent capability. Older than the Tornado and rather less manoeuvrable, it has a longer range and similar weapons-aiming and navigation avionics. It lacks the versatility of the Anglo-German/Italian aircraft.

Specification:
Length overall: 22.40m
Wingspan: 19.20m
Maximum speed at sea level: 793 knots
Combat radius hi-lo-hi: 1480km
Maximum weapon load: 11340kg
Take-off distance: 914m

Assessment
Manoeuvrability	***
Rough-field capability	*
Robustness	***
Range	*****

The F-111 has earned itself a formidable reputation for accurate bomb delivery and low-level penetration.

attack, increasing the vulnerability of the aeroplane. This vulnerability is reduced by using effective tactics – approaching the target at minimum height and from an impenetrable or lightly defended direction.

Tornado is tailor-made for the extreme requirements of all-weather, low-level attack in Europe's hostile environment, strengthening NATO's deterrent posture by providing vital support to the ground forces.

An RAF Tornado gets airborne. With afterburners engaged, the Tornado's two RB.199 turbofan engines produce more power than the engines of nine wartime Gloster Meteor jet fighters.

the Tornado with its rivals

F-15E Strike Eagle

The new McDonnell Douglas Strike Eagle is packed with the very latest avionics for the ground attack and interdiction role. Derived from the F-15 Eagle air superiority fighter, the Strike Eagle retains a phenomenal performance, particularly at high altitude. The aircraft's large wing, optimised for dogfighting, gives the aircraft a very poor ride at low level, reducing the aircraft's usefulness in the low-level role.

Specification:
Length overall: 19.43m
Wingspan: 13.05m
Maximum speed at sea level: 790 knots
Combat radius hi-lo-hi: 1200km
Maximum weapon load: 10,659kg
Take-off distance: not released

Assessment
Manoeuvrability ★★★★★
Rough-field
capability ★★
Robustness ★★
Range ★★★

The dual-role F-15E Strike Eagle will soon enter service with the US Air Force in Europe.

Su-24 'Fencer'

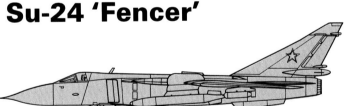

Designed from the outset as an all-weather, low-level attack aircraft, the 'Fencer' bears a close resemblance to the F-111, although it is rather smaller. Little is known about the aircraft, and estimates as to its performance vary enormously, although it is indisputably a very capable machine in its intended role. Several specialised variants of the aircraft have been identified.

Specification:
Length overall: 21.29m
Wingspan: 17.50m
Maximum speed at sea level: 790 knots
Combat radius hi-lo-hi: 950km+
Maximum weapon load: 11,000kg
Take-off distance: (estimated) 762m

Assessment
Manoeuvrability ★★★
Rough-field
capability ★★★★
Robustness ★★★★
Range ★★★

The Su-24 'Fencer' is probably the most capable Soviet attack aircraft ever produced.

MiG-27 'Flogger-J'

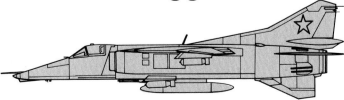

The MiG-23 and MiG-27 'Flogger' family is in service in enormous numbers with the air forces of the Warsaw Pact and with client nations in the Third World. The top-of-the-range 'Flogger-J' is comprehensively equipped by Soviet standards, but its avionics lack the sophistication and reliability of those fitted to the Jaguar.

Specification:
Length overall: 16.00m
Wingspan: (swept) 8.17m; (spread) 14.25m
Maximum speed at sea level: (estimated) 725 knots
Combat radius hi-lo-hi: (estimated) 390km
Maximum weapon load: (estimated) 4,500kg
Take-off distance: (clean) 2,200m

Assessment
Manoeuvrability ★★★
Rough-field
capability ★★★
Robustness ★★★★
Range ★★

As a low-cost, low-level attack aircraft, the MiG-27 makes a lot of sense despite its poor performance.

Bruiser from Brno

When the war ended in 1945 the Czech army had to pick up the pieces and re-organize itself, but before it could get very far the country fell under Soviet domination and the Army, like other Soviet satellites, adopted Soviet weapons. This did not suit the Czechs, who had ideas of their own, and some very good designers, so it was not long before they began developing their own weapons.

Among the most pressing needs was a pistol; their pre-war design was a horrible weapon, and anyway most had been taken by the German army, and the current issue pistol was the elderly Soviet Tokarev. So the designers were put to work to produce a decent pistol, and the result was the CZ52, an odd design with a most complex roller-locked breech: really locked, unlike the Heckler & Koch roller system, which is only a delayed blowback. In spite of its complications, its difficult manufacture and its undoubted cost to produce, it has remained the issue Czech army pistol ever since, and it remained in production until the mid-1970s.

The CZ52 satisfied the army but it did not satisfy its makers, since it had

Above: The alert position. This pistol has the advantage that it can be carried cocked and locked, or hammer down at half cock with a round in the chamber. The double-action trigger pull is surprisingly smooth, and the first round fired double-action does not print too far away from the rest of the group fired single-action.

The 15-shot magazine provides serious firepower and gives the pistol good instinctive pointing qualities with a grip that fills the hand. Women with very small hands may find this a problem.

Above: The CZ 75 shoots comfortably even with military 2z ammunition, and will happily feed semi-jacketed soft points as well as the full metal jacket ammunition it is designed to shoot.

Right: External dimensions of the pistol are similar to the Browning, so it will fit military holsters. Note that the earlier models have slightly shorter slides: make sure you select the long-slide version when buying.

no export potential: largely because of its complexity, but also because it was chambered for the Soviet 7.62-mm pistol cartridge, which nobody outside the Soviet bloc used. The first attempt to improve matters was the model 50, a 7.65-mm blowback more or less copied from the Walther PP. This, due to bad manufacturing technology, proved to be unpopular and unreliable, but it is still the principal pistol for Czech police and security forces.

Best shot

The next attempt was the CZ75, generally agreed to be the best pistol to come out of Czechoslovakia in the last 50 years. Here the designers turned to the best time-tested ideas, and assembled a reliable and accurate weapon. The locking system is pure Browning, using a shaped cam beneath the breech, and two ribs on top of the barrel which lock into the roof of the slide. The lockwork allows single or

Double tapping with the CZ 75: a case in the air and the pistol rock steady back on target. It shoots well, and is entirely adequate for combat use. At full recoil the pistol hardly moves off target. This technique is known as the 'combat crouch'.

double-action firing. The magazine holds 15 rounds of 9-mm Parabellum, and the pistol is well-proportioned and sits comfortably in the hand.

The first models were carefully and slowly made by machining solid steel billets to make the frame and slide, but this was too expensive so they used investment casting. This was beyond Czech technology at the time, and the first cast components were imported from Spain. Eventually the Czech factory perfected the casting technique, and the pistols were made entirely in Czechoslovakia. Early machined pistols have a slightly different frame contour to the cast models, and they are also identifiable by having the front face of the trigger grooves.

In the endeavour to reduce production costs, some bureaucrat ordered that the half-cock notch on the hammer be removed, since he could see no purpose for it. After loads of reports from West Germany of accidental dis-

Inside the CZ75

Imitation is the sincerest form of flattery, and the CZ75 has been copied more frequently than any other modern pistol. The Italians have made a bargain-basement copy, the TA 90; the Swiss have an up-market copy and a cut-down police version. The design also formed the basis for the excellent but ill-fated Bren 10 pistol. The pistol is now available in a product improved version, the CZ85, with ambidextrous controls and better finish.

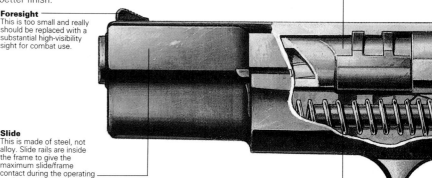

Barrel
The barrel is made of steel and locks into the top of the slide when the weapon is ready to fire and during the first part of the recoil, after which the breech drops down to allow the slide to move backwards separately.

Foresight
This is too small and really should be replaced with a substantial high-visibility sight for combat use.

Slide
This is made of steel, not alloy. Slide rails are inside the frame to give the maximum slide/frame contact during the operating stroke.

Recoil spring and guide
This is one unit: do not pull it apart. The spring forces the slide forward, chambering a round and locking up the barrel into the slide. The spring is compressed by the force of the exploding round after the breech is unlocked, when the breech pressure has dropped to an acceptable level.

Trigger
The trigger is linked through a split trigger bar which runs either side of the magazine well. Pulling the trigger through when the hammer is down will cause the hammer to rise and fall, i.e. fire double action.

Stripping the CZ75

1 Remove the magazine, rack back the slide and eyeball the chamber. Remember, this pistol does not have a magazine safety, so it will fire a round without the magazine (unlike the Browning).

2 There are two lines cut in the back of the slide and frame. Match these up by pulling back on the slide with one hand and lock the slide in position with the safety catch.

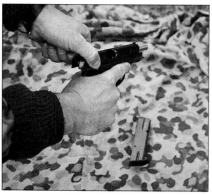

3 On the right-hand side of the pistol is a button where the slide stop pin protrudes out of the frame. Press this in firmly: you may need to use the base of the magazine.

4 You can now pull the slide stop out of the frame on the left side. This disconnects the slide assembly from the frame.

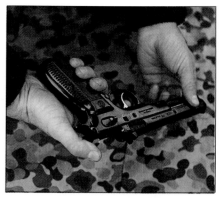

5 Now take the safety catch off, squeeze the trigger and drop the hammer. The slide assembly will slide off forwards from the frame.

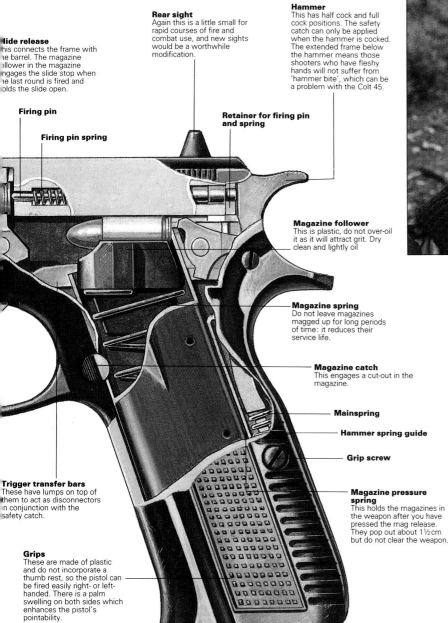

Slide release
This connects the frame with the barrel. The magazine follower in the magazine engages the slide stop when the last round is fired and holds the slide open.

Firing pin

Firing pin spring

Rear sight
Again this is a little small for rapid courses of fire and combat use, and new sights would be a worthwhile modification.

Hammer
This has half cock and full cock positions. The safety catch can only be applied when the hammer is cocked. The extended frame below the hammer means those shooters who have fleshy hands will not suffer from 'hammer bite', which can be a problem with the Colt 45.

Retainer for firing pin and spring

Magazine follower
This is plastic, do not over-oil it as it will attract grit. Dry clean and lightly oil

Magazine spring
Do not leave magazines magged up for long periods of time: it reduces their service life.

Magazine catch
This engages a cut-out in the magazine.

Mainspring

Hammer spring guide

Grip screw

Trigger transfer bars
These have lumps on top of them to act as disconnectors in conjunction with the safety catch.

Magazine pressure spring
This holds the magazines in the weapon after you have pressed the mag release. They pop out about 1½ cm but do not clear the weapon.

Grips
These are made of plastic and do not incorporate a thumb rest, so the pistol can be fired easily right- or left-handed. There is a palm swelling on both sides which enhances the pistol's pointability.

The pistol out of the box is sighted in for a target at 25 metres. The sights are perhaps a shortcoming, as they are a little too small for a really clear sight picture. However, for slow fire work the sights are useable.

charges, the half-cock notch was rapidly restored to the design.

The quality of manufacture and finish on the CZ75 is well ahead of any other pistol produced in postwar Czechoslovakia, and after its introduction in 1976 it sold well in Germany and other European countries. It shoots well, is robust and reliable, and the cost is attractive when compared with Western products.

Copies of the CZ75

An additional income has been the licensing of manufacture outside Czechoslovakia. One such licensed copy is the Swiss AT84. However, the Swiss have made some minor but important modifications; the AT84 safety catch works whether the gun is cocked or uncocked, whereas the CZ only renders the pistol safe when it is cocked. The Swiss design has adopted

6 The frame should not be stripped further. The recoil spring and guide is removed from beneath the barrel by pushing forward and lifting it up and then withdrawing the spring and guide to the rear.

7 The barrel will drop down and is removed from the slide to the rear. Make sure you clean the barrel and the feed ramp. You can strip the firing pin and spring out of the slide, but there is no need for normal cleaning.

8 The weapon field-stripped clearly demonstrates its lineage from the Browning High Power. However, the CZ75 is an improvement in several respects over the Browning classic, which has after all been soldiering on since 1935.

When the last round is fired the slide is held open. Note that with the slide moving inside the frame there is no chance of the novice causing jams by resting his thumbs on the slide.

To release the slide, you can either press down on the slide release or pull back the slide. If you have just reloaded, keep your finger off the trigger when you press the slide release.

a custom-made German Peters-Stahl barrel of exceptional hardness and accuracy. The finish is of the highest order, better than the CZ product.

New developments

However, the Czechs were not content to sit on their design, and two years ago they introduced the CZ85 model. This is the 75 brought up to date by incorporating an ambidextrous safety catch and slide stop. The top of the slide has been ribbed to cut down reflection and give a clearer sight picture, and some minor changes in the lockwork have resulted in a smoother trigger-pull. The finish of this pistol is really first-class, and it

Battlefield Evaluation: comparing

CZ75

This is a good, solid combat pistol straight out of the box. It has a surprisingly smooth double action, and the improved CZ85 model has ambidextrous controls and a better finish. The only area of complaint are the sights, which are in need of improvement. The Brno shows that Eastern block manufacture does not necessarily mean dodgy quality, but it does mean a very attractive price tag.

Specification:
Cartridge: 9-mm Parabellum
Muzzle velocity: 340 metres per second
Weight: (empty) 980g
Overall length: 203mm
Barrel length: 120mm
Magazine capacity: 15

Assessment
Reliability ★★★★
Accuracy ★★★★
Age ★★
Worldwide users ★

Above: The CZ 75 is an excellent combat pistol, now followed by the CZ85 pistol at a very attractive price.

Steyr GB pistol

The gas-delayed blowback action of the pistol, and its size, make recoil easier to control when shooting heavy service loads than some conventional designs. The sights have the three-dot feature for rapid sight alignment and give a good, clear sight picture. The gargantuan magazine capacity is always of value in military terms but makes the pistol a little bulky for concealed carry.

Specification:
Cartridge: 9-mm Parabellum
Muzzle velocity: (depending on cartridge used) 360-420 metres per second
Weight: (empty) 845g
Overall length: 216mm
Barrel length: 136mm
Magazine capacity: 18

Assessment
Reliability ★★★★
Accuracy ★★★★
Age ★★
Worldwide users ★

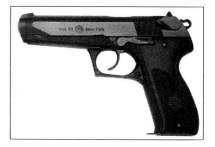

The Steyr GB pistol is gas-operated, which considerably reduces felt recoil.

Browning High Power

The Browning is a classic that can still be measured among the best combat pistols on the market. Fabrique Nationale of Belgium have now introduced an improved double-action version which brings the design up to date. The pistol's controls are generally a little too small to be fumble-free, especially the safety catch, and the sights are again small for combat use.

Specification:
Cartridge: 9-mm Parabellum
Muzzle velocity: 350 metres per second
Weight: (empty) 810g
Overall length: 200mm
Barrel length: 130mm
Magazine capacity: 13

Assessment
Reliability ★★★★
Accuracy ★★★★
Age ★★
Worldwide users ★★

The Browning is a reliable performer, and in spite of its age has few disadvantages in combat use.

remains to be seen how well it will do in the commercial market.

Strange as it may seem, the CZ75 has not been adopted by the Czech army or police forces; it is entirely for export, to gain much-needed hard currency. Also there may be sufficient CZ52 and 83 models (the 83 replaced the 50, and is no more than a slight improvement on it), to satisfy military and police needs. Certainly the 75 and 85 could not be adopted as they stand, since the 9-mm Parabellum is a Capitalist cartridge, not to be tolerated in a good socialist state; but it should not be beyond the capability of the Czechs to remodel the 75/85 into 7.62-mm if they really wanted.

The bad news as far as speed reloads goes is that the CZ 75 does not eject the empties out of the gun like the Colt 45. They have to be helped out, and that will cost you valuable fractions of a second.

The correct way to make the weapon ready. You can then drop the magazine and top it up so that you have 16 shots to play with: twice the capacity of the Colt 45 Government model.

the CZ75 with its rivals

Bernadelli P-018 pistol

This latest offering from Vincenso Bernadelli is a robust 9-mm double-action 15-shot semi-automatic pistol designed for the police and military markets, of excellent quality and all-steel construction. The sighting system uses the three white dots for rapid alignment and the trigger guard is shaped for the two-handed grip. The only weak element in this exceptionally compact and strong design is the heel of the butt magazine release, which some may not care for.

Specification:
Cartridge: 9-mm Parabellum
Muzzle velocity: 350 metres per second
Weight: (empty) 998 g
Overall length: 213 mm
Barrel length: 122 mm
Magazine capacity: 15

Assessment
Reliability   ★★★★
Accuracy   ★★★★
Age   ★
Worldwide users ★

The Bernadelli is blighted only by the heel of the butt magazine release, which slows up speed reloading.

Walther P88

This is a well-built, large capacity double-action 9-mm designed for the military and police market with several typically Walther features: it has an ambidextrous decocking lever for dropping the hammer, which also acts as the slide release. There are a number of safety features built in, which means that the only way the weapon will fire is by pulling the trigger.

Specification:
Cartridge: 9-mm Parabellum
Muzzle velocity: 360 metres per second
Weight: (empty) 900 g
Overall length: 187 mm
Barrel length: 102 mm
Magazine capacity: 15

Assessment
Reliability   ★★★★
Accuracy   ★★★★
Age   ★
Worldwide users ★

The Walther P88 has abandoned the stylish lines usually associated with Walther products.

Walther P5

The quality of this pistol is clearly demonstrated by export orders which include USA, Nigeria, Portugal and several South American countries. The German police tests demanded a very high standard of safety in handling, and the P5, although conventional in other respects, is unique in having four different built in safety systems. Its compactness makes it more concealable than its large-capacity competition and more suitable for some police tasks.

Specification:
Cartridge: 9-mm Parabellum
Muzzle velocity: 350 metres per second
Weight: (empty) 795 g
Overall length: 180 mm
Barrel length: 90 mm
Magazine capacity: 8

Assessment
Reliability   ★★★★
Accuracy   ★★★★
Age   ★★
Worldwide users ★★

The Walther P5 is perhaps more suitable for police use than any of the other pistols shown.

Tracking for Survival

As a soldier, your knowledge of tracking will enhance your awareness, increase your ability to gather intelligence, and sharpen your fieldcraft. If you are in command during extended border operations, a tracking capability will enable you to build an accurate map of the localised enemy movements without having to send out large numbers of patrols.

But for a survivor, tracking skill means food. If you're close to civilisation, man-made obstacles such as fences and irrigation channels force game to pass through bottlenecks, making trapping easy. But in remote, sparsely populated areas, it is not so simple. You must be able to recognise the trails of local game and be capable of following them from their resting

Tracking skills are a very useful addition to your infantry skills. With a competent tracker in your team, follow-up after an ambush can be done at speed without dogs and with or without a blood trail to follow.

Your tracking kit

You should not need any specialist equipment, but the following will simplify your task.

1 Notepad and pen
This is a very important part of any track pack: a detailed drawing of the track you are following can easily be photocopied and distributed to other trackers. While learning to track, make frequent drawings. This will force you to notice the fine details in any footprint, such as wear patterns and sole damage, which will enable you to pick it out again later.

2 Map and compass
These not only show you where you are: they will often enable you to guide in a strike force or tracking team to cut the trail of the target and eventually intercept. Take your eyes off the trail frequently and study the map, to try and understand where your target might be heading. For example, if he is heading for a waterhole you may be able to insert a heliborne troop to ambush him.

3 Watch
An important navigational tool. By acting out the target's trail for a given distance, you will be able to work out his speed of travel.

4 Torch
This will enable you to control the light under difficult conditions and to track at night. The torch must be robust and ideally have a soft focus capability, which reduces the fatigue of 'eye strain' during extended night tracking.

5 Tracking stick
This is a unique tracking aid developed by the trackers of the US Border Patrol. On the stick are two adjustable markers, which are used to measure the step interval and track length. When you have difficulties finding the next track you should find the next sign at the point of the stick.

6 Lollie sticks
These are used to mark each track, enabling you to see at a glance the track pattern.

7 Orange crepe paper
This can be used to mark a trail, or a particularly interesting aspect. Again, this is favoured by the US Border Patrol. If a tracking team comes across a forgotten marked trail it is difficult to confuse with a fresh trail as crepe paper fades quickly.

8 Mine tape
This can be used to mark the start of the trail and sets of tracks of great importance. Always remove mine tape at the completion of the follow-up.

9 Magnifying glass
A very useful aid to tracking, although you will not use it as constantly as Sherlock Holmes might!

10 Binoculars
The use of binoculars is not always possible, but they can sometimes be used to read tracks at a distance as well as for making visual contact with the target.

How to mark up a print

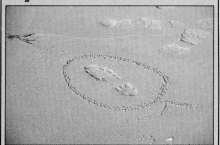

Once you have found a print, mark it up as shown: a semicircle with a tail on the right indicates a right foot, and a tail on the left of the semicircle is a left foot.

At the end of every trail is a target. The tracker's job is to follow the string of clues to catch it. An experienced tracker should be able to build up a good intelligence picture of the target.

areas to their feeding areas, where trapping is easier.

Good trackers are rare. When they are needed for military purposes, commanders usually employ hunters from the local indigenous population. But this does not mean that Westerners cannot track; some of them are among the world's best trackers. A tracker is a reader of 'sign'. He takes a few faint pieces of information and, by the process of deduction and comparison with previous experience, puts the puzzle together.

The more experience the tracker has, the better able he is to do the job. But he must still beware the following:

1 Lack of confidence
Even the best trackers use intuition, and a tracker must know when to trust a hunch. With lives at stake, lack of confidence can cloud your ability to think straight. Experience is the only solution.

2 Bad weather
'Sign' does not last for ever. Wind, rain and fresh snowfall will all obliterate it: many a trail has gone cold because the tracker has not paid enough attention to the weather forecast. With unfavourable weather imminent, short cuts may need to be taken to speed the 'follow-up'.

3 Non-track-conscious personnel
By the time trackers are called in to follow a trail, the clues at the proposed start have usually been destroyed by clumsy feet. If you are fortunate enough to work with a team that can recognise 'sign', even though they cannot read it, you will have extra pairs of eyes to help you find the vital clues.

4 Unsympathetic commander
Tracking is a solitary business, requiring great concentration. A tracker must have the trust of the commander, and must be able to trust his cover

Using the tracking stick

The first mark to set on your stick, using the moveable rings, is the step interval. This is the distance from the tip of the toe to the heel of the opposite foot.

The second mark you set on your stick is the foot length, measured heel to toe. This is set from the step interval mark. If you can't find the next print, you put the first marker over the toe and rotate, and the next heel print will be under the point.

If you find a heel mark but can't see the toe, all you have to do is put the second marker over the heel and rotate the stick. The tip of the toe should be under the first mark.

Tracking exercises

dog

fox

cat

deer

Roads produce a continual harvest of wild animals: careful examination of the corpses yields vital information for the tracker. Note how the fox pad has fine, prominent hairs sticking out beyond the pads: this sometimes shows in tracks.

You need hundreds of hours of practice and regular tracking exercises. The following are designed to equip you with the basic skills. Practise them as often as you can, in as many different environments as possible. Try to spend three hours on each exercise each time, and record your progress in your log.

1 Familiarise yourself with the track diagrams. Imprint their shape in your memory, paying particular attention to the details. Now try to find real examples of these tracks, draw them and measure them.

2 Having found the tracks of the animals represented, try to find out as much as you can about them by following the trail. Don't be disappointed if you lose the trail early on; this is a vital part of the learning process. Make a detailed drawing of the last two tracks you can find. When you've learned more, you may be able to decipher the clues to the next track.
3 Find out as much as you can from books about the animals represented. What do they eat? Where do they live? What noises do they make? What do their droppings look like?
4 With a teammate, compete to see who can

find the most feathers lying on the ground. Now identify which birds they belong to. If you come across a heap of feathers indicating a kill, try to discover which predator was responsible.
5 Follow a well-worn trail and see how many hairs you can find.

---

group. Tracking often seems to be painfully slow, but the tracker will be moving as fast as he can: never rush him. The more intelligence he has at his disposal, the better, so tell him what is going on: your knowledge of enemy movement may make sense of an otherwise meaningless clue.

Try to allow the tracker time to impart a rudimentary knowledge of tracking to his cover group, and make sure the cover group are all patient men: the tracker has the challenge of the trail to hold his attention, but the cover and support group does not. If they make any noise, it is the tracker who is at greatest risk.

Learning to track

Tracking is not a particularly difficult skill to learn, but it needs dedication and much practice. Once you have learned the basic principles and

Becoming sign-conscious

The first skill of tracking is the most important one you will learn: becoming sign-conscious. There is no quick way to achieve this. As you go about your everyday business, try to notice footprints, tracks, fingerprints, hairs and other signs. As you walk along a pavement, look out for the elastic bands discarded by postmen.

At first this will be a contrived activity, but with perseverance you will begin to notice these fine details in the overall pattern around you without thinking about it. When this happens, you are ready to start tracking.

techniques you can practise in your own time. If you want to reach a high standard, it will help if you have a team mate who can lay trails for you. Make sure you keep a log: this must include the duration of the track, the time of the day, the ground conditions, and the level of difficulty.

Teaching yourself is not easy. The biggest mistake you can make is to 'run before you can walk': for at least your first 50 hours, follow simple trails, concentrating on accurately interpreting the 'sign'. Then gradually increase the difficulty of the trails. When you have 100 hours under your belt, you should be following fairly difficult trails.

Reading 'sign'

You're unlikely ever to find a string of 'Man Friday' footprints. Instead you will have to follow a trail of scuffs, creased leaves, bruised grass stems, hairs and occasionally part of a footprint.

If you are lucky enough to find a clear print, study it carefully to glean as much information as possible about the target. Compare it with your own to determine the target's size, sex, age, weight (load or no load), speed of travel, and whether he is fit or exhausted.

You must also be able to read animal signs, even when tracking people. For example, a human track with a badger print on top of it will show that the track was made before the badger was active at night. If you

know the habits of the local wildlife, you will have gained a clue to the age of the track.

Animal tracks may also lead you to a rubbish or food cache, providing you with crucial information regarding the target's state of mental, moral and physical well-being.

Attributes of a tracker

Tracking is mainly a visual skill. Your eyesight, whether you wear glasses or not, must be 20/20. Short-sighted people often seem to make good trackers once their eyesight is corrected.

A general ability to observe is not enough for tracking: you have to piece information together, like Sherlock Holmes. You must also be patient, persistent and constantly questioning your own theories, especially if you are 'solo tracking'.

Very often, you will trail your target to within touching distance. To reduce risks, self-defence and close-quarter battle skills are vital.

Although modern equipment plays an important role in the task of tracking, remember that it does not replace your tracking ability: it just makes life easier.

Clothing and equipment

A tracking team must be totally self-sufficient and capable of operating as an independent unit. Communications equipment and plenty of supplies and ammunition must be carried. Tracking can often be a slow process, so everyone must be warm, windproof and waterproof.

The tracker's load is normally carried by the support team, leaving him with only his belt kit. Make arrangements for his kit to be dropped where he can reach it at the first sign of trouble.

Tracking teams are vulnerable to attack, so flank protection is vital. Here it is being provided by a South African Army trooper armed with an R4.

Marking up the track pattern

Mark each footprint as taught and make a detailed sketch of the prints in your notebook. To get a better view of the pattern of the target's movement, mark each print with crepe paper, lolly sticks or similar.

This marking gives you a better idea of where to look for the next print if you are having problems. A Polaroid camera is a good idea for recording tracks, especially if you are using more than one team.

Using the Light

In order to track successfully you must learn how to position yourself to make best use of the available light. This track is seen with the sun behind you: this is wrong.

A South African Defence Force tracking team looks for signs of guerrilla movement. This task is particularly difficult as the sun is almost overhead.

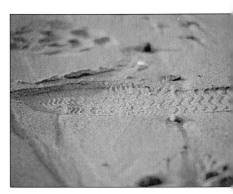

Do not view the track from the side. It is clearly visible in this example, but finer sign would not be seen.

Now that you have become more sign-conscious, you must learn to maximise your chances of seeing sign. To see the greatest detail in a clear print you need contrast: this means the light striking the ground at a low angle. Normally, this means that you are limited to tracking when the sun is low in the sky, during the morning hours and in late afternoon/early evening. Around mid-day the light is almost directly overhead and casts a flat light, which makes ground features disappear. However, time will usually be against you in most live tracking situations, forcing you to continue through the mid-day and sometimes even into the night. In this case you will need to make use of techniques that have been devised to control the light conditions to your advantage.

Daylight tracking

When the sun is low in the sky, you can take advantage of the light just by positioning yourself correctly: **make sure the track is between yourself and the light source** by watching the shadows cast by your tracking stick. Probably the most common error of novice trackers is to align themselves incorrectly.

Once you are in the correct posi-

tion, it is often an advantage to lower your line of sight, sometimes even right down to the ground. As you become more proficient you will do this mainly for seeing the finer details or when the light is bad. If you are not used to squatting on your haunches for long periods, include exercise for this in your fitness programme: novice trackers on their first extended follow-up often miss sign due to a reluctance to squat down.

When you are sign-cutting (searching for sign, normally aiming to cross the target at 90°), getting into the correct position relative to the sun is vital, but can pose problems. If the target is moving directly away from the sun, to 'follow up' you will have to look back over your shoulder. This must be practised, as it takes some getting used to.

If you have to follow up through the mid-day period, you will have to slow down and be more careful, which is more tiring. Ideally your commander will use several trackers and rotate them at point duty.

You may be able to gain some lighting advantage by using your torch. A

The same track is seen from the correct angle: the track is between you and the light source the sun.

torch is also the best answer when you are tracking in woodland where the light conditions can be very confusing, especially under dappled shadowing.

Night tracking

Night tracking is not always possible; it depends on the local ground conditions. Because you will be using artificial light you can precisely control the light angle. Wherever possible, try to position your light source low and with the track between yourself and the light. A torch with a variable focus beam can be an advantage. If you are using vehicles on dirt roads fit them with tracking lights, set to point sideways, creating contrast lighting.

Night tracking should play an important part in your training programme as it helps to reinforce your use of light and enhances your ability to notice sign. Study clear prints as well as faint sign, and experiment with the light angle and beam focus until you feel you have the correct combination.

At night, your ability is severely handicapped by the change of colours to monochrome. In tactical situations, follow-ups usually only continue at night when a life is at risk or if there is a high probability of changing weather conditions obliterating the available sign.

Tracking on a slope

Many novice trackers fail to notice that the ground conditions are chang-

ing from flat to slope because they are too wrapped up in the sign: even the very gentlest slope will dramatically affect the lighting conditions, sometimes favourably, sometimes not. There is little you can do except to be aware of the situation.

Moisture can often make tracking

The tracker is cutting for sign: that is, looking for tracks. The shadow shows he has correctly positioned himself. The tracking stick can be used to find the best angle by holding it out and looking at the shadow.

The squashed grass shines and clearly shows the target's footprints. The short step interval shows that he is carrying some weight. Again, early morning or late afternoon is the best time to observe this.

Light is vital to the tracker. The best times to track are early morning or late afternoon, where the low angle of the sun brings up the track. It is possible to track using artificial light by securing a torch to the end of your tracking stick and holding the torch on one side of the track while you read it from the other. Here, poor light results in the target being lost. This position is known as the LPC (last point of contact).

Survival

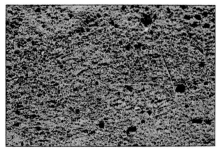

Above: The correct viewing angle for the track: the shape of the boot heel and sole can clearly be seen.

Military footwear tends to be very robust and easily crushes or bruises vegetation. The weathered surface of the sandstone has been clearly scraped by the heel. This sloppy foot placement tells you that the target is moving at speed.

To correctly position the light you may have to track looking back over your shoulder. Here you have to watch out that you do not accidentally destroy sign.

easy. Dew that collects on surfaces, particularly plant foliage, will normally reflect light well. Places where a target has stepped will usually show as dark patches if he flattened down the vegetation before the dew settled, because the light will reflect off these patches at a different angle from the surrounding vegetation. However, if he passed by after the dew settled it will have been wiped off the vegetation.

On hard, flat surfaces such as rock, moisture can reveal the prints of the target as light patches. The dust on the surface will darken with moisture, but he will have removed dust by treading and so the moisture will not collect so easily.

Remember, don't just watch the ground. Sign can be left by any part of the body: for instance moisture missing on a shrub may give you an accurate indication of the target's height.

Tracking by feel

You will usually be tracking by sight, but you may find yourself in situations when a track cannot be seen – although this does not mean that it can't be detected.

A track in short grass is an example. When a foot treads on grass, the grass is flattened and sometimes broken,

The target has trodden on the root, leaving a damp patch. This should immediately grab your attention, more so than the obvious print; the target is close.

If you walk round the track so that you are viewing it from the same side as the sun, the track disappears.

Tracking through low cover

Tracking through low cover requires attention to detail at two levels: the ground, for vegetation crushed and disturbed by the feet, and waist height for damage caused by the equipment the target is carrying.

The stringy sap from the broken bracken stems tells you that the target is close.

After a few hours the sap stains the crushed pieces of fern brown.

bruised or torn. Greater damage is caused when the target is travelling at speed or under a load. If not too badly damaged, the grass slowly recovers, to stand upright again. The time it takes for the grass to untangle itself and recover will depend on the local weather conditions and the variety of grass. It does not usually take long for the track to become invisible to the eye, but some blades of grass will remain depressed.

By very light and careful probing with the tips of your two little fingers, you will be able to detect these blades of grass by a resistance to your probing. Compare this with the surrounding area. With care, you should be able to discern the overall shape of the track.

Other signs

Do not make the mistake of looking only at the ground. Search also for other signs such as bruised vegetation, scuffed roots, broken cobwebs, pebbles turned to expose their darker, damp underside, and the smallest of details such as grains of sand deposited on large pebbles by the target's boot.

To become a successful tracker you must pay attention to all of these factors all of the time. These signs combine with the tracks to fill in the missing details in the mental picture you are building of your target. In a tactical situation, your life and those of your teammates may depend on your noticing a few grains of sand.

Tracking exercises

Represented here are another set of animal tracks with which to familiarise yourself. Repeat exercises 1-3 of the first set of tracking exercises for these new animals. Pay particular attention to the way by which they form a pattern of tracks.

1 Find a piece of bare earth or sand, smooth it over and make a set of tracks inside it; do not make the tracks too obvious. By packing the ground hard you should be able to achieve a very fine impression.

Make a careful study of this impression at different times of the day: mid-morning, mid-day, mid-afternoon, dawn and dusk. Observe the track from the shadow side, the sun side, and with the sun to your side. Make drawings of the track under all of these circumstances, being careful to draw only what you can see.

2 With the same track impressions, experiment with your torch. Draw what you can see with the torch between yourself and the track, with the track between you and the torch, and with the torch illuminating from the side. Position the torch to point along the ground and also down onto the ground at about 30°. Finally, draw what can be seen with the torch directly above the track, with both hard and soft focus.

3 Armed with your tracking stick, tape measure, notebook and torch, follow the trail paying careful attention to the light. Ask a teammate to stop you randomly to check that you are correctly positioned in relationship to the light. In bad shadows or under a forest canopy, experiment in improving the light with your torch.

4 With a teammate, study a track: firstly while standing, secondly while squatting down, and thirdly when on all fours and your head next to the ground. In each case, record the details you observe.

5 Follow an animal trail with your teammate. Try at first to find 10 tracks, then 20, and so on up to 100. When you are able to do this, repeat all these exercises in different conditions (remember, the more challenging the terrain the more you will be learning).

Fighting Fit

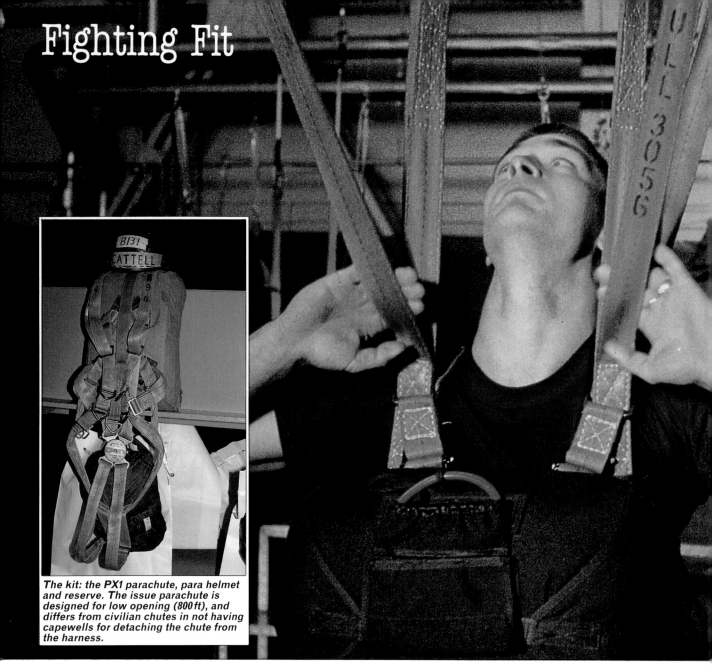

The kit: the PX1 parachute, para helmet and reserve. The issue parachute is designed for low opening (800 ft), and differs from civilian chutes in not having capewells for detaching the chute from the harness.

What it takes to be a Para
"1000, 2000, 3000!"

Friday of Week 16 sees the conclusion of Advanced Wales and the platoon in preparation for the move on Sunday to Royal Air Force Brize Norton. The authority to train all Airborne Forces in Britain is vested in the RAF, and is carried out at No. 1 Parachute Training School (No. 1 PTS) at the major airbase near Oxford.

The aim of the course is to train and qualify the Regular Airborne Soldier in all aspects of basic parachuting techniques, so that he can operate as an effective member of an airborne assault force.

After Aldershot and the rigours of Advanced Wales, Brize Norton is a virtual paradise. As the coach enters the main gate and continues down the long road towards your accommodation, you wonder if you are hallucinating. You pass a Naafi, bar and nightclub complex called 'The Spotlight'. There is a swimming pool and sauna, and even a 12-lane bowling alley! The cookhouse has the grand-sounding title 'The Cotswold Restaurant' and promises delights unheard-of at the Depot.

It is a mystery to you why the RAF should live in such comparative

luxury, especially when the coach pulls up at what is to be 'home' for the next four weeks. The barracks here are modern, red-brick buildings. Nearby is a row of ancient green-painted huts. The new blocks are for the RAF; you are pointed towards Hut 425.

A mixed bag

That evening the platoon is joined by a transferee, a former member of the Royal Anglians whose training was interrupted by his having to return to his old unit in order to finalise his transfer papers. He is soon accepted into the close-knit commun-

The badge of
The Parachute Regiment

Check canopy! Look for the perfect circle of canopy; anything less and you have a problem. If it is a line-over or twists then you can sort it out, but remember that you haven't got a lot of time to waste. If in doubt, use the reserve.

ity of 531 Platoon.

Besides the Parachute Regiment's 26 recruits, Basic 956 will also comprise a PARA 2nd Lieutenant; a number of Royal Marines; 7 RHA; Royal Corps of Signals; REME; RCT; and even one or two volunteers from the Catering Corps!

Small groups

Your first Monday at Brize Norton begins with introductory lectures. Everyone is bunched together and then broken down into squads of seven or eight individuals irrespective to their units. Following the introduc-

tion routine, you move across to the nearby hangar of 1 PTS to be shown around the various training aids. Taking centre stage is a mock-up of a Hercules aircraft fuselage, used for rehearsing emplaning, seating and exit drills.

Training kit

In one corner is the 'Fan' or Exit Simulator. Another corner is occupied by two dozen parachute harnesses dangling in six rows from the ceiling rafters high above. Gymnasium mats surround the Hercules mock-up, around which almost all aspects of ground training will take place. You are also shown the parachute PX1 Mks IV and V and the harness, before moving swiftly into the first steps of ground training itself.

Rotating lessons

Besides your own course there is also another Basic Course in progress. The various groups rotate around the hangar's different stances, spending a minimum of 30 minutes on each lesson. With several classes being taken simultaneously it can get extremely noisy inside the echoing hangar. You need to shut out all that is going on around you and concentrate solely on the lesson in hand.

Like all aspects of military instruction, parachuting is entered into gradually. Initially you are shown the basic exit, flight and landing – or Immediate Action (IA) – drills. Exit

The parachute roll. On hitting the ground the points of contact should be: feet, calf, thigh, round of the backside, and the back. Remember to keep your feet and knees together, knees bent and head down on your chest.

drills are first explained in detail, and then practised in step by step lessons. After adopting the correct exit position – without equipment, this is standing with arms folded and head tucked well in – you leap forward off a

A student clips into his harness assisted by his oppo. All quite a performance: even worse when you realise that part of the dropping into water drill involves getting out of the harness while hurtling towards the deck!

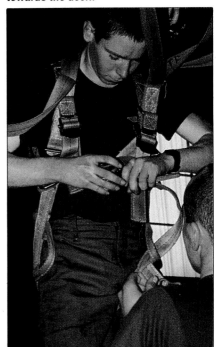

One real danger in military parachuting is hitting the para next to you. You get out of the way by steering your chute, pulling down on the straps.

low bench, landing on the flat of your feet. Easy.

Following this simple introduction, you can start on flight drills. You practise these suspended in a parachute harness. An instructor explains the drill for a variety of situations: how to react in the event of your drifting towards, across or below another parachutist, for example. You rehearse the movements again and again and again. Each flight period begins with the checking of equipment (whether or not you are actually wearing any)! You then exit the (imaginary) aircraft.

Check canopy

'Red on,' shouts your instructor, 'GO!'

'One thousand, two thousand, three thousand.' Everyone counts off the three seconds for the canopy to deploy.

'Check canopy!' You then shout, and look up.

'Canopy okay,' the instructor advises, 'Carry on. All-round observation; push the front two liftwebs to one side, both over, both sides; then look down through your legs ... Right ... there is a parachutist directly underneath you!'

'Steer away!' you shout in warning.

Assess your drift

'That's it. You can use any lift web to steer away as the parachutist is underneath you. Okay, you are in clear airspace, carry on ... look down and assess your drift ...'

Landing drills are carried out initially with the student adopting a parachute position on the ground. You stand with feet firmly together, knees slightly bent, chin tucked well

into your chest and with arms raised as though grasping the lift webs. The object of the exercise is to rehearse you in the various landings to be encountered: side left/right, front left/right, back left/right ... The instructor calls out the type of landing, and you respond by performing a para roll in that direction, gently twisting your body into the movement and following it through as taught.

Right-hand roll

For example, during a side right landing, you begin the roll by pushing your hips to the right. The part of your body to first touch the ground during the roll is your right calf, followed by the side of the thigh, and right buttock. You follow the roll through, up the side of the back and back of the shoulders and over to the left, bringing your legs up and over towards that side so that you finish curled in a U-shape on your left side.

Exit Simulator

As soon as you have grasped the first elementary lessons, you progress a stage further. Having learned how to exit an aircraft correctly at ground level, you can try it from slightly higher! The Exit Simulator allows you to experience something of the feeling of a parachute descent. Several harnesses are each attached to their own cable, the ends of which are wound around drums attached to large fans on a platform 10 metres above the hangar floor. As a cable is unwound, it turns a large fan which dictates the speed at which the cable can be let out, depending on the force exerted.

Out of the doorway

The platform loosely resembles an aircraft fuselage with several exits along its side. After climbing a ladder onto the platform you strap yourself into a harness and a dispatcher directs you to the doorway. On his command you launch yourself forward through the opening. The big fan whirrs into motion, and you find yourself descending at a rate approximate to a parachute descent. As you are falling straight down, though, it is awkward to carry out a satisfactory landing, and almost everyone ends up in an untidy heap on the mats below.

After just three days you are considered ready for your first parachute jump. The first is almost always a balloon descent, made from a steel 'cage' suspended below a huge oval balloon, 250 metres above the Drop Zone. Weather permitting, this will take place first thing next morning.

In civilian parachuting, you exit the aircraft in the stable spread position. But when you are carrying kit this is the position you use.

Combat Report
Angola:
Deep Penetration Operation Part 1

In 1980 Neil Anderson, a member of the South African Defence Force, took part in a deep penetration operation into hostile Angola, to search and destroy known guerrilla bases some eight miles across the border.

The operation was in response to the massacre of a small settlement where guerrillas had shot the inhabitants and then burnt the bodies, not caring if they were black or white.

We had been told that there would be little opposition, as the guerrillas were poorly armed. Captain Ryan had said, "It's just a case of in, hit them hard and out . . . simple." We were also told that the Russian and Cuban advisers, who were known to be in the country, were in the north and that we were unlikely to meet them. But it wasn't going to be that simple.

The recce patrol returned

Getting the 40 men over the border into Angola was easy. There was no-one there to stop us. Our first task was to bivi up for the night and then send out a recce patrol to scout for enemy activity. Purely a listening patrol, they were instructed not to engage the enemy unless absolutely necessary. We didn't want to give ourselves away at this stage in the operation.

The recce patrol returned two days later, reporting that they'd found two camps. The first one contained about 20 guerrillas who were lightly armed with AK-47s and had only one transmitter. Despite this, they appeared to feel very secure as they hadn't posted any sentries and were making a lot of noise. In fact, that was how the recce patrol had managed to locate them so easily.

About five miles further north, situated near a dirt track, was the second camp. This time there were approximately 40 guerrillas. Once again,

they were lightly armed and had no sentries. Litter had been scattered everywhere, and two 3-ton Bedford Lorries were parked nearby. This looked like a permanent camp. It was probably a jumping-off point for guerrillas who were to attack the neighbouring states.

Captain Ryan, an ex-Rhodesian SAS officer, decided that we would first take out the smaller camp, search the dead and wounded, and then move on to the second target. We would then make for the LZ where our choppers would fly us out.

The march to the first target was uneventful. As we came within 200 yards of our quarry Captain Ryan signalled the patrol to go to ground in all-round defence. He then went and had a look. After about 20 minutes he returned, happy with the situation. Two cut-off groups, consisting of one gunner armed with a GPMG and three riflemen, were deployed to the left and right flanks of the target. Then the rest of us moved slowly towards the target, creeping forward until it was in full view. Our information had been correct; they were all just sitting around, either drinking beer or just chatting to one another. Although some had their AK-47s slung over their shoulders, most had them on the ground beside them.

It was a tank

Captain Ryan was the first to open fire, followed closely by the rest of us. The terrorists who had their weapons slung over their shoulders returned fire almost immediately, but most of the others were cut down while trying to reach for their firearms. It was all over in a matter of seconds. Captain Ryan shouted, "Cease fire," and the only remaining sounds were from the two cut-off groups as they fired at a few guerrillas attempting to escape. Four men went forward to search the bodies, then we moved on to the next target.

We did exactly the same here. Once again the information from the recce patrol appeared to be correct. One man was asleep, leaning against a tree-trunk with an AK-47 beside him

Tracking down the SWAPO guerrillas in Namibia was no easy task. They operated in small groups and scattered if menaced by the security forces.

while the rest just milled around or chatted and smoked. All appeared quite normal – until we opened fire.

For the first few seconds we had the upper hand. Then suddenly, out of our view, a heavy calibre machine-gun opened up on us, killing two of our section instantly. We then saw about 70 Cuban soldiers going to ground in front of us, at the same time putting down some accurate fire. It was obvious that their fire and movement tactics were far superior to the guerrillas'. It was so intense that we literally had to bury our noses in the ground.

Captain Ryan ordered us to pull out – one order that we didn't hesitate to follow. The only way we could leave our position was to crawl out backwards, keeping our bodies as close to the ground as possible. A couple of lads threw smoke and HE grenades, but that was futile as they couldn't raise their heads high enough to see where to throw them. Then I heard the sound of a powerful diesel engine and a metallic clatter. One of the lads saw it before I did. As he said, "Oh, ****," I looked up – it was a tank.

The guerrillas believed they were safe in Angola and paid little attention to security. We advanced into one of their camps completely undetected.

As this frontier post shows, we were not the first to cross the Angolan frontier packing hardware rather than passports.

Fighting Fit

The badge of
The Parachute Regiment

A member of staff explains the benefits of life insurance to a course member. Every drop produces some casualties, but thorough training for when things go wrong keeps the figures down. Virtually every paratrooper will be injured at some time in his career: it is simply a question of when, and how badly.

What it takes to be a Para
THE BALLOON JUMP

You wake up to Day 4 of parachute training and immediately have a look outside. It's a beautiful, clear morning. Ideal parachuting weather! After a wash and shave you pull on your work clothes and saunter across to the 'Cotswold Restaurant'. For some reason, breakfast isn't so appetising this morning.

You return to Hut 425 and tidy it up before filing outside to wait for the coach that will take you to the training hangar. You de-bus for the usual muster parade and then half of you re-board the coach that will take you to the drop zone at RAF Weston-on-the-Green.

The remainder of the course will follow in another coach 1½ hours later, by which time the first batch should have nearly completed jumping.

Barrage balloon

The trip out is rather quiet and, apart from some joking among the RAF instructors, lacks the usual cheery banter. After nearly an hour you suddenly catch sight of a huge silver object hanging motionless in the still air. The thing resembles a World War II barrage balloon.

You stare as the coach turns off the main road, passes through the camp gate, and pulls up alongside a group of trucks. The balloon is attached by a cable to a winch on one of the vehicles. A blue metal cage is suspended immediately below the balloon. An airman strides across to the bus. The door opens and the RAF hold a hasty conversation.

This is it, you think to yourself. Here we go. You have mentally prepared yourself and, despite the horror

The balloon: jumping from this is the most terrifying part of the training course. Up there it is deathly quiet, and the ropes stretch away uninvitingly to the ground.

*Hopkins, number 3 in stick **A**, looks a little apprehensive as he watches A2 plummet towards the ground from the balloon basket. The helmets are marked so that everyone maintains the correct order and the staff get to know who they are shouting at.*

stories dished out by the Depot training staff, you know that you'll jump when the time comes. This is what you've been working towards now for four months! Apart from anything else, the shame would be unbearable. You *will* jump. You hope. Well, let's go then. Let's get it over with.

The winch man, who had stepped outside to chat with his RAF colleagues, re-boards the coach. He tells you they're having problems with both winches. You might not jump after all.

After all the mental preparation this

Checking equipment is a very time-consuming business, which gets even worse when you are introduced to the delights of container packing.

news comes as an awful anti-climax. You peer out of the coach windows at the dejected-looking group gathered about the RAF vehicles. The instructors discuss the problem over steaming cups of tea.

Then there's movement outside. What's going on now? One of the winches has been fixed! Okay, lads, you're to jump after all! A sudden hollow, empty feeling in the pit of your stomach. But first the whole ensemble has to be moved to the other end of the Dropping Zone (DZ) due to a change in wind direction. More delays.

Into the cage

At last everything is in position and ready for the first lift. This will consist of RAF despatchers, who will show you how it's done. They climb into the cage and in a few minutes are lifted 800 feet above your heads. You watch them fall at intervals of a few seconds. Down comes the balloon. Into the cage clambers the first of the Course. The others watch the proceedings and, again, everything goes well.

Eventually it's your turn. Four of you kit up and walk across to the balloon. A cheery despatcher ushers you into the cage and, one by one, secures each static line to a strongpoint just aft of the exit. There's no door as such, simply an opening with a thin metal bar across it.

"Up eight hundred," says the despatcher, "Four men jumping".

The balloon begins to rise. As the ground falls gently away nobody says a word.

"Anyone know any jokes?" asks the despatcher.

Don't look down

The balloon slows to a halt. It's suddenly very quiet. The despatcher grins.

"Okay, let's have the first of you. Step forward. That's it. Two hands on the bars here . . ."

You grasp the vertical bars projecting from each side of the exit.

"Right, remember, both arms across the reserve . . ."

That empty gut feeling again. You stare straight ahead. Don't look down. Don't look down. Don't . . .

"GO!"

Automatically you launch yourself forward and through the door space. Automatically you bellow the count, but much too fast.

Below: The reserve. If you have a problem, the drill is – feet and knees together, pull the handle, grab the contents and throw it down and away so that it does not foul what's left of your main chute. Be prepared for a real jerk when it pulls you up.

Fighting Fit

Some worried faces on the line up before walking out to the balloon. Certain hard characters who have strolled through P Company have failed at this point.

"One thousand two thousand three thousand . . . ooph!"

You plummet two hundred feet before the breath is knocked out of you as your parachute deploys. "Check canopy!" Hastily you look up, ensuring that the canopy is fully deployed. It is! Relief!

You relax slightly. The view from 500 feet is almost as good as at 800.

You look around and marvel at the sensation as you slowly drift earthwards. All too soon the ground is rushing up to meet you. Bang! A bit of a bumpy landing, but you're still in one piece.

Reserve 'chute

Quickly you carry out the Harness, Release and Drag (HRD) drills. Undo one clip of your reserve. This allows you to roll onto your front and collapse the canopy by grabbing and pulling in half a dozen lower rigging lines. When the canopy deflates, drag

in the rest of the parachute. Tuck it under your chest and then turn onto your back again, lying on top of the canopy to prevent it from reinflating.

Wriggle free

Next, twist and hit the Quick Release Fitting (QRF) to enable you to wriggle free of the harness. Stand up and pack away the whole ensemble. An instructor yells at you:

"Get a move on there, and double away off the DZ!"

Your first jump is over. Nothing to it!

Broken pelvis

Later that day someone from another syndicate is involved in an aircraft descent when a colleague drifts across his parachute, stealing the air and collapsing his canopy. The subsequent plunge from 75 feet results in a broken pelvis for the unfortunate soldier. This is a forceful reminder that parachuting is a dangerous business, to be accorded the respect it deserves. A lesson none of you will forget in a hurry!

In the cage at 800 feet, the normal combat jump height. Don't forget to count and check canopy as you exit. You can scream later. It looks too close to the ground and, if things go wrong, you have limited time to deploy your reserve.

Combat Report

Angola:
Deep Penetration Operation Part 2

Neil Anderson of the South African Defence Force continues his story of a raid into Angola in 1980.

I had never realised how menacing a tank could look, especially if it happens to be an enemy one that is coming towards you. As the barrel began to traverse, I knew there was no option but to stand up, risk being hit in the back, and run like hell. The rest of the section obviously thought the same, as we all stood up together, just as I was looking at the two lads running parallel with me, there was a sudden loud 'boom' as the tank opened up. To this day, I do not know if those two soldiers received a direct hit. All I can say is that one moment they were there and the next they had gone. It was as if they had never existed. After that I ran even faster. I don't think there is an athlete in the world who could have caught up with me that day.

We were now out of range of the small arms fire, but the tank was still bombarding us with shells, and one or two mortars had also joined in. Still running, we could hear the shells and mortar bombs whistling towards us. The most terrible thing was being able to hear the shells but not see them, and all the time expecting to be hit.

I had a head start

The time had come to split up. We had a better chance of survival if we all made our own way to the emergency RV. After what seemed like an eternity, I found myself alone and mercifully out of the tank's range, which gave me a moment to assess my situation.

I knew I had to figure out how I was going to get back over the border. We had been briefed on the location of emergency RVs, but I was apprehensive. I knew we had suffered casualties, but I didn't know how many. Also, some wounded had been left behind. What if the enemy forced one of them to reveal where the RV was? I could find myself walking into an ambush. Although I trusted my fellow soldiers, I was realistic. I knew that if the enemy captured

Some SADF missions against the guerrillas used captured Communist bloc weapons, in this case RPG-7 anti-tank rockets and PK GPMGs.

any of them, they would do their damnedest to make them talk – the Geneva Convention doesn't exist in this part of the world.

However, I couldn't spend too much time wondering what to do next. I had a head start on the enemy and had to move before they tracked me down. I decided to make for the RV and watch it until I was satisfied that I wasn't walking into an ambush. If there was any doubt about it, I would make for the border.

Although I'd been trained in escape and evasion tactics, I'd never dreamt that I would actually have to put them into practice. I was apprehensive about the Russians and Cubans, especially the former, who have fought in numerous areas. If they were tracking me, I would have to use my evasion skills to the utmost.

As I walked, I made sure I left no traces of my presence – upturned stones, broken branches and footprints – but I still had to move fast. What if they had tracker dogs? I tried to dismiss this idea, but couldn't. I remembered what a British soldier had once told me: "You cannot fool a well-trained dog, but you can fool its handler." I reflected on some of the methods he had mentioned and decided to try them. I ran as fast as I could and then jumped up in the air. My distance would never win a gold medal, but it might make a dog lose the scent for long enough to make the handler think the dog was confused. I then ran a large zig-zag, followed by a few more jumps. Then I walked for a few miles in a straight line towards the RV, alternating with with the zig-zags and jumping, until I thought I'd done enough to get any dog handler pissed off.

The snapping of branches

I carried on like this until it began to get dark, then I decided to lay up for an hour or so. First, though, I doubled back and sat behind a clump of bushes for about 40 minutes, just listening for the sound of approaching footsteps. Fortunately there were none, so I made my way back to the place where I'd decided to lie up.

This had plenty of bracken, providing an excellent deterrent against a dog plus good concealment. I crawled into the bracken and made myself as comfortable as possible. The only equipment I had was an automatic rifle,

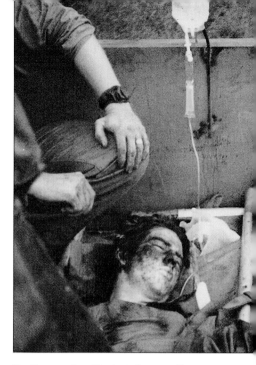

Heavily outnumbered by the various guerrilla formations and the armies of the 'front-line states', the SADF made maximum effort to save its wounded and repatriate captured personnel.

four magazines, a knife, two water bottles, a 24-hour belt, a medical kit and some basic survival equipment. I ate a bar of chocolate, being careful to put the wrapping paper in my pocket, and drank about two mouthfuls of water. Although I was very thirsty, I needed to conserve as much water as possible.

Suddenly there was the snapping of branches, the pounding of heavy footsteps and the harsh breathing of men. I was now as frightened as I had been when confronted by the tank, but to my relief, after what seemed an eternity, the footsteps faded. In reality, it was probably only about 10 to 15 minutes. I decided that although the enemy was about, I would have to move under cover of darkness. I was lightly equipped and could move slowly to avoid any undue noise.

I walked for three hours, all the time using my evasion techniques, until, just as dawn was breaking, the RV came into sight. There was no apparent sign of life so I walked in cautiously, only to be greeted immediately by Captain Ryan. During the next hour or two, we were joined by 19 of my Army mates.

The covert raids of 1980 and 1981 were followed in 1982 by Operation Protea, a full-scale invasion that inflicted substantial casualties on SWAPO.

Fighting Fit

The badge of
The Parachute Regiment

What it takes to be a Para
"RED ON! GO!"

Your first parachute descent from an aircraft is scheduled for the Tuesday of your second week at Brize Norton. But when you get to the training hangar you're told that the jump has been postponed due to unfavourable weather conditions. The news is half expected, but you're disappointed nevertheless.

The morning is spent rehearsing flight and landing drills. After lunch you return to the hangar and are faced with another delay while Course 955 gets in a para drop: your DFC (draw and fit 'chutes) is fixed for 1415 hrs,

and you are to be ready to emplane at 1500. In the meantime you are taken for more ground training!

Hanging in the air

Once again you find yourself suspended in a harness a metre or so above the hangar floor, with an instructor providing numerous imaginary scenarios for you to react to. You rehearse the drills for a tree landing; for drifting towards a building; for landing in water ...

You look down and assess your drift. You're having a nightmare of a

time and find you're at 200 feet and drifting towards water ... You're at 150 feet ... 100 feet ... 80 ... 50 ... 20 ... feet touching the water ... NOW!

During the countdown you feverishly undo your harness until you are supported by the seat straps. As soon as your feet touch the water, you unclip one side of the reserve and slip out of the harness. Simple! Now, one more time to make sure you've got it.

At last the time arrives for you to kit up. First, though, you're given a short briefing on what to expect, including a rundown on emergency, flight and listening to the roar of the four big propeller engines.

When everyone is seated the aft door closes. Despite three rows of ceiling lights it's still quite dim inside the aircraft. There's a faint smell of Aavtur aviation fuel, reminiscent of the helicopter flights two weeks previously. The noise from the engines is terrific. There's a subtle change in pitch and the aircraft begins to rock gently. Then it moves, bouncing and trembling, towards the runway.

There's a distinct change in engine pitch as power is increased. From somewhere underneath you comes the sound of mysterious bangs and

way. The red light snaps on, followed a moment later by the green. The instructor disappears. He is known as the "drifter" and will allow himself to descend at the mercy of the wind in order to assess its strength and direction. This assists the pilot in correcting any error for the run-in when the troops are dropped.

Action stations

All too soon the Hercules has circled and is making the next approach. By now the first stick is hooked up and standing at 'Action Stations'. The lead man stands at the door, one foot forward, one hand across his reserve and the other along the top edge of the door. The ground rushes past 1,000 feet below. Occasional gusts of cold wind snatch at the sleeves and trouser legs. The red lamp blinks on.

"RED ON!" yells the despatcher.

Stomach muscles clench.

The red light snaps off and is instantly replaced by the green.

"GO!"

The first stick shuffles toward the

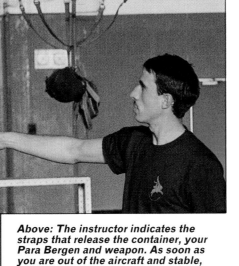

Above: The instructor indicates the straps that release the container, your Para Bergen and weapon. As soon as you are out of the aircraft and stable, away from anyone else, you drop the container on its strap.

Main pic: Practising parachute landing fall positions. Your arms reach up for the straps and your head is down on your chest as you look down to assess your drift relative to the ground.

landing drills. The RAF officer concludes with the usual "Any questions?" There are none.

"Have a good one," he tells you. "You've been waiting long enough."

Kitting up

Along one side of the hangar are two long racks supporting your parachutes and helmets. You pull the heavy equipment on and are then checked by the PJIs.

Just before 1500 hrs the C-130 Mk III Hercules lands and taxies across to the hangar. You file outside, board the big aircraft and a PJI allocates you a seat. You fasten the seat belt and wait,

thumps. Everyone acts nonchalant, apparently unconcerned. The power is increased further, the engines roaring as the mighty aircraft accelerates along the runway before lifting slowly into the air. Your ears instantly begin to pop with the sudden change in air pressure. You're acutely aware of the angle of flight as the pilot climbs before finally levelling out.

Prepare for action

The despatchers now warn both port and starboard sticks to prepare for action. There then follows a series of checks and double-checks, ensuring that everyone's equipment is correctly and securely fitted.

As the aircraft approaches the Drop Zone (DZ) the port side door is opened, letting in a sudden rush of chilly air. A PJI moves into the door-

You endlessly practise getting out of the aircraft when you see that green light. You exit with your body compact, protecting your reserve; that way arms and legs do not get in the way of the chute as it deploys.

Fighting Fit

In the yawning rear door of the Hercules you get plenty of time for second thoughts. On a combat jump the combined weight of kit and parachutes will make walking out to the aircraft a real challenge.

exit. Your turn arrives and suddenly you are outside the door! For an instant it feels almost as if everything has stopped, but you're acutely aware of moving down an invisible slide as the slipstream catches you: a weird mixture of sensations. As you fall you catch a glimpse of the Hercules disappearing at a seemingly crazy angle.

"One thousand, two thousand, three thousand!"

The canopy deploys, jerking you upright and knocking the breath from your body.

"Check canopy"

Automatic drills

You look up at the big, green circle above your head. The shroud lines are all okay; no twists. Carry out the flight drills, as taught. It all comes automatically. The long hours spent inside the hangar have paid off! You have a few moments to enjoy the sensation of slowly drifting Earthwards, then the ground suddenly rushes up at you. You pull down on the correct lift webs in order to slow the final rate of descent.

The idea is that, in a front-left landing for example, the rear lift webs are pulled down allowing air to spill from the front of the canopy and to remain trapped in the rear, thus slowing the descent. You let go of the lift webs only when your feet touch the ground.

Despite what you may have been told, an actual parachute landing *is* harder than one made from the "fan". Yet, unlike the fan, the parachute's drift allows you to perform a satisfactory roll. No bones broken. You get

out of the harness, pack away your parachute and double away off the DZ. Great! Your first aircraft descent is over!

After completing one balloon and three aircraft (clean fatigue) descents, you are nearly ready for your first equipment drop, but before making a real parachute descent you have to rehearse an equipment jump from the Outdoor Exit Trainer (OET). The OET is not the most pleasant of experiences and is appropriately referred to as the "knacker cracker".

Varying loads

Then onto the aeroplane descent. For training purposes, the equipment container is a stone-filled jerry-can. The weight of each varies considerably – from about 15 kg to over 30 kg! Who ends up with what depends largely on luck. The container is secured to your thigh until after you have exited the aircraft, when it is lowered at the end of a five-metre line.

Despite the worrying sight of the

The moment of truth: if you refuse to jump at this point you are out. You cannot afford to hesitate in combat. Any delay means you will not land together or off target, which will leave you vulnerable.

heavy load swinging below, it is rare to actually land on the thing. When the container hits the ground you are still drifting, however slightly, overhead. Therefore you will (nearly) always land alongside it.

You had hoped that your OET training would be your last taste of the "knacker cracker". You were wrong.

The stick drifts towards the ground. Your main problem at this stage is avoiding other people, finding some space and dropping your container.

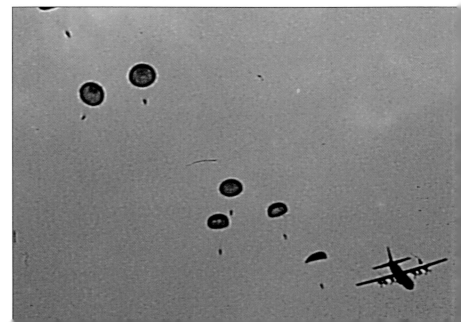